Recipes an

ETHIOPIAN
Foods and Drinks

Including Spices and Herbs

For Your Taste, Pleasure and Good Health
By Getty Ambau
Author of Alternative Health

Copyright © 2016

Cover art and illustration by Philip Howe of Philip Howe Studios

Cover arrangement by Getty Ambau

Typeset by Greg Brown

Library of Congress Control Number: 2015920054

ISBN: 978-884459-06-1

Published by Falcon Press International

Important Note

The information contained in this book is meant to be used for educational purposes only. It is not meant to replace the advice or consultation of a trained professional. Additionally, the medicinal properties of some of the herbs and spices mentioned in this book, is not to suggest that you use these substances, in the place of exiting, scientifically-tested drugs, to treat an illness or cure disease.

Dedication

Art by Daniel Getahun

To my mother and the generations of Ethiopian women
who created the many wonderful foods and drinks we enjoy today.

Contents

PART I
Ethiopian Cuisine

Ethiopian cuisine

An introduction

"Ethiopians slept for a thousand years, forgetful of the world by whom they have been forgotten." So said Edward Gibbon, the noted 18th century British historian, referring to Ethiopia's isolated existence for so many centuries.

Bounded by a scorching desert in the southeast, a deep and wide sea in the north and north-east, rugged terrain in the west, and largely inimical Muslim countries and enclaves all around, Ethiopia had led a slumberous existence, indeed, as far as its engagement with the outside world was concerned. Yes, outsiders had visited Ethiopia at different times, but rarely the other way around. A few Ethiopian emissaries had visited European cities in the late 1800s.

Some who read this quote out of context are bound to believe that Gibbons must have been referring to the country's lack of progress in the thousand years it had slept. That certainly is not the case.

Ethiopia has had progress in all its cultural elements: cuisine, religion, language, music, social customs, and the arts. Let me cite a few examples. The 6th century scholar, Yared, is a cultural icon who developed the educational system, contributed to Ethiopia's literary heritage, and composed much of the church music in use to this day.

Over the hundreds of years, the country has produced a great many artistic and literary works. Unfortunately, much of what was written or produced remained in the hands of the Orthodox Church, impacting the creativity or artistic expression of the average Ethiopian very little. Also, most of the literature was written in *Ge'ez*—an ancient language which only the learned men of the ecclesiastical institutions understood. Secular education was nonexistent until about a hundred years ago. Even after that, though, pursuing education outside of the church schools was considered sacrilegious. In this regard, Gibbon was probably right in his perception of Ethiopia's state of affairs.

Amharic (Ethiopia's national language) is perhaps one of the most sophisticated languages in the world. It has a rich vocabulary. Words can have or be made to have, depending on one's mental acuity, different shades of meaning. Through a system of poetry called *sem-ena worq*—wax and gold, the literal and figurative (or the obvious and hidden) expressions—what appears a compliment can turn out to be actually an insult or criticism. Someone's simple commentary turns out to be an observation on universal truths or wisdom. And like most poetry, it's the gold that often moves the spirit, delights or saddens the heart. This form of expression has evolved over time.

The culinary arts, on the other hand, were a different matter. The Ethiopian woman (yes, food preparation and cooking was the exclusive domain of the female gender) had no constraints. She was limited only by the extent of her talent and imagination. Because of this freedom that the women enjoyed, we have a great variety of some of the most sophisticated dishes in the world.

"Ethiopian women can make as many as seven hundred-fifty or more dishes," one woman once told me.

How?

Spices!

The Ethiopian woman combines many different spices to create dishes as distinctly different from each other as beef stroganoff is from Peking pork chops.

She also uses food preparation techniques such as aging, smoking, and drying to bring out distinct aromas and flavors in foods, and the dishes that are prepared from these ingredients are often succulent, zesty, and healthy.

As researchers around the world are finding out, spices have many beneficial properties. Their antioxidants help protect the body against cancer, heart diseases, diabetes, and other degenerative conditions. The vibrant shades of red, yellow, orange, brown and other colors that are often seen in Ethiopian spices represent their component phytonutrients. These compounds, have many wonderful benefits. You can see on the back cover of this book a sample of the spice colors found in Ethiopian foods.

Traditionally, there is no standard recipe book. Nothing is written down. Each family has its own way of making its own dishes, usually inherited from the older generation. Yes, there are a few common ingredients found across the board: onions, garlic, coriander, cloves, cinnamon, etc. What a woman can add beyond these constituents, and their proportions, becomes her propriety.

The most common Ethiopian foods are *injera* and *wot*—sauce. The injera is the *crêpe*-like bread made usually from fermented *teff* flour. Particular to Ethiopia, teff is a small grain which usually comes as either white or brown or a mixture of the two, called *sergegna*. The wot can be made from the flour of legumes—pea, chickpeas, or fava beans—called *shiro*, and meats—chicken, lamb, or beef. It can be mild, middle of the road, or spicy hot. The spiciness depends on whether it was made with *berbere*, which is the foundation of many Ethiopian dishes. See the ingredient list for berbere in the Selected Ethiopian Food Recipe section.

These dishes are what may be referred to as traditional for most country folks; the dishes and how often they are prepared and consumed depends on the economic status of the household. Shiro wot and injera are the most common. Injera by itself or with a*waze*—a paste made from berbere and water—can be all that a poor person has to eat sometimes; at other times, just the injera by itself if they are in a dire situation. For vegetables, *gomen*—collard green and potatoes—are most common.

Nowadays, in cities and towns, a green salad with tomatoes, and mixed vegetables—consisting of cooked potatoes, cabbage, and carrots with homemade cheese on the side—often accompany the main dishes.

Why Ethiopian food is healthy

For those who are careful about what they eat, Ethiopian foods have many attributes that make them appealing.

The spices and herbs used to prepare Ethiopian foods are rich in antioxidants, phytonutrients, vitamins, and minerals. As you have read about these food components earlier in the book, these nutrients are very beneficial to the body.

Ethiopians fast over 200 days out of the year and break their fast only with vegetarian foods. Because of this practice, many Ethiopian cuisines appeal to vegans and also to those whose constitution is sensitive to fats and animal products. Only vegetable oils are used for cooking for the fast foods.

Ethiopians rarely eat sweet foods. Desserts are not common, although now restaurants have begun offering a few selections for those customers who have to have a dessert after their meals. You don't have to worry about loading up on too many sugar calories when you dine at an Ethiopian home or restaurant.

Regarding the absence of sweets in the Ethiopian diet, I'll share a couple of anecdotes. When I went home to visit my family several years ago, I brought with me a few Hershey's chocolate bars, thinking they would be a special treat from America for the neighborhood kids.

A couple of days after I arrived I gathered up the children and gave a chocolate bar to each. They first inspected the wrapped objects and then one by one started to tear the paper off after I urged them to do so. All the children held the bare bars and stared at them, unsure of what they should do, even after I told them what they were, emphasizing how delicious they were. To allay their concerns, I peeled off the wrapping from my own bar and started to munch on it.

One brave soul placed the end of his bar into his mouth and took a bite. Seconds later, his face went sour. His lips twisted. "Ughhh." He immediately turned his head away and spat it out. Others took a bite of their bars, sank their teeth into them, but just as quickly their expressions also went sour, and they, too, spat their bites out. After I calmed down from hearty laughter, I asked each what it was they didn't like. They all said the candy was too sweet.

The other testament about the excessively sweet American diet concerns my own experience with dental caries. I had never had cavities before I came to the United States at 19 years of age, but within six month of my arrival, I got two of them.

The only time white sugar is used in Ethiopia is with tea or coffee. Even this practice is a recent phenomenon. Where I grew up, we either drank our coffee without any sweeteners or with fragments of a salt bar. Sugar was just not available to folks who lived in remote places.

The low calorie, low fat diet, together with the use of spices and herbs in food preparation are major factors why Ethiopians, on the whole, are healthy people. Obesity, heart disease, cancer, and diabetes are almost unheard of. With the introduction of Western-type diets, however, the health picture of the population is bound to change for the worse in due time. In the cities this is happening already. And Ethiopians who live in Western societies have been getting these food-related diseases in greater numbers. For example, one study of the Ethiopian community in Israel found "within just a decade a relatively high prevalence of diabetes (10 to 17%), which was literally unknown to it prior to (their) immigration."

Ethiopians don't use processed or frozen foods. These things are a product of modern technology. To taste good and wholesome, the foods have to be prepared fresh from whole grains and vegetables. However, because pure teff flour is sometimes finicky to turn into good injera in the Unites States, some restaurants may constitute the teff dough with white wheat flour. Temperature, humidity, baking temperature and even altitude can affect the fermenting dough from which injera is made.

Ethiopian foods have a good amount of fiber—teff, as you will see later, contains a great amount of roughage, important for the health of the GI tract.

This book is to serve the reader primarily as an educational tool. Although I have included recipes for foods, it's not meant to be used as a major reference source for a wide range of dishes. There are other books for that and I've included the titles of a couple as well as links to web sites at the end. This book is about the benefits of the most common ingredients found in Ethiopian dishes.

White sugar, white flour, soft drinks   Teff, Mitten Shiro, Berbere, 4 Pillars Foods & Drinks

Fewer   More

⟵ [   ]   Number of Essential Nutrients Consumed   [   ] ⟶

Nutrition Continuum

This nutrition continuum illustrates the four possible levels of nutrition and serves as a model that accommodates individual differences and nutritional need variabilities among humans.

The 4 pillars above refers to vitamins, minerals, fiber and phytonutrients. These are very critical for good health and wellness.

CHAPTER 1
Teff

Teff is a highly nutritious grain that has been cultivated in the highlands of Ethiopia starting sometime between 1000 B.C. and 4000 B.C. Now it's also grown in the United States and Australia, and probably in other countries as well. It's a tiny grain—150 granules of teff is equivalent to one kernel of wheat—yet, nutritionally, as you will see below, teff offers so much. Teff comes in many different varieties, but the most common are brown and carmine red. The white variety is more expensive than the others but in the homes of well-to-do families in Ethiopia, it's the most desired. Nutritionally, though, the brown and red varieties offer much more than the white teff.

Teff is a very good source of protein, including some of the essential amino acids that one usually finds in animal products like whey or eggs. Reportedly, a 2-ounce serving of teff can contain as many as 7 grams of protein, which is equivalent to that found in an extra-large egg. It's said that daily consumption of one injera crêpe supplies enough of the amino acids to sustain life without another protein source. This explains why many Ethiopians who don't consume milk or eggs or meat during fasting or even non-fasting times, show no sign of nutritional deficiency.

Furthermore, a cup of teff can provide 14.7 mg or 82% of the daily value (DV) of iron and 347 mg or 35% DV of calcium. Reportedly the iron from teff is better absorbed than that found in other grains. Teff therefore can be good for menstruating women or anybody who doesn't get sufficient iron from their normal diet.

That same cup of teff can contain up to 356 mg or 89% DV of magnesium and 828 mg or 83% DV of potassium. And it has a whopping 17.8 mg or 892% DV of manganese. This quantity of teff also contains high amounts of copper and zinc—78% and 47% of DV, respectively, and smaller amounts of selenium and sodium. A cup of teff provides 16 grams of fiber.

Vitamin-wise, this same cup of teff was found to contain between 30% and 50% DV for thiamin, riboflavin, niacin, and Vitamin B6. Interestingly, we also expect to find 261 mg of omega-3 fatty acids and 1807 mg of omega-6 fatty acids. These fatty acids, as you saw earlier, are very important for good health and vitality.

Teff has a low glycemic index, only 84. Twenty to forty percent of the carbohydrate contained in teff is resistant starch, meaning that much of the carbohydrate is not available to the body. Both these attributes should be appealing to diabetics and those who wish to lose or manage weight. Teff is gluten free, which make it a desirable food for people who are sensitive to gluten (a form of protein found in wheat, barley, and rye), a condition referred to as celiac disease. When people with celiac disease consume foods that have gluten, their body mounts an immune response that attacks the small intestine. These attacks disrupt the normal absorption of nutrients into the body.

One writer described the white teff as having a chestnut-like flavor and the brown, a slight taste of hazelnut. I'd describe the white as somewhat nutty and the brown as slightly tart and sweet.

You should now see why teff is indeed such a remarkable grain. In the years I have been reading and writing about nutrition, I often wonder about the good health of my family from Ethiopian highlands, where there are no fruits or vegetables, which are normally the good sources of vitamins, minerals, phytonutrients, and fiber. Yet these people seem healthy and fit. All this has to do with the four pillars of health they find in teff, and in the peppers and spices. Nearly all of them are lean because they work hard and walk a lot.

How you prepare and consume teff

Traditionally, the teff dough is fermented to make injera. Because certain vitamins are produced during the fermentation process, the nutritional value of the food is enhanced during this process.

Ethiopians generally use teff flour. You can use the whole teff with soups, cereals, and other such dishes. Even then, you will be better served if you use teff flour. You shouldn't try to make flour by grinding whole teff in your blender or coffee grinder. The grains are way too small for these machines. It's better if you purchase teff flour at a health food store or an Ethiopian market and use it to make bread by itself or to replace a quarter to a third of the wheat flour you use to make loaves, cakes, and other bread products. You can also make porridge out of teff flour: sprinkle it with berbere or salt and red pepper powder (to taste), and serve.

In a recipe, if you're substituting teff for nuts, other grains, or seeds, use only half as much teff as the full measure of the item you're replacing, because the teff granule is so small.

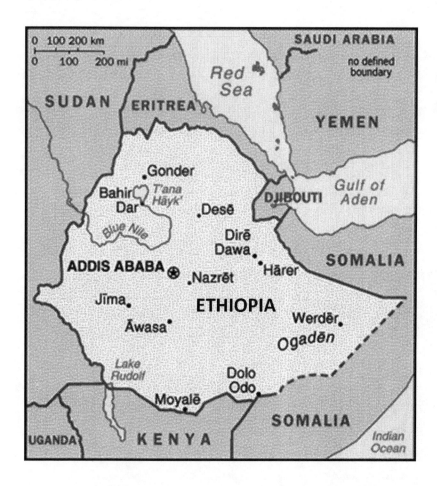

**An ancient country, rich with history and traditions,
the birthplace of coffee, teff and many flavorful and healthy foods.**

Ethiopian spice samplers

PART II
Ethiopian spices

CHAPTER 2
Abesh (Fenugreek)

Abesh is one of the main ingredients in many Ethiopian spice formulations. By itself it's used to flavor injera, and as part of other spices, wot and other dishes. As you will see below it's also often made into a drink.

Like all the spices we use in our foods, most people may think that abesh's role in dishes is merely as a food-flavoring agent and a beverage. As you will soon see, abesh actually has many benefits for your health, good looks, and longevity. The great flavor you're trying to impart to your dish by including abesh and other ingredients in it is only part of the full story.

First, let me just say that abesh seeds have intrigued me since I was a boy. A groove runs nearly diagonal across its rectangular slab-like shape. A hook drops down onto one edge of the seed, which used to remind me of a bird's beak. The seeds appear neither true gold nor yellow but somewhere in between, with a texture of marble.

These seeds are rock-hard to chew on and taste bitter if you manage to crack one of them. As if to make up for the deficiency in taste, though, they smell somewhat sweet. I often wondered what the deal was with abesh, that my mother always included them in her spice concoctions. Now, from the studies I have done, I know that abesh's hardened exterior and unpleasant taste are only a facade. These golden-yellow seeds, which Westerners call Fenugreek, have many health benefits.

Abesh grows worldwide in semi-arid regions such as the Mediterranean, western Asia, northern Africa, the Middle East, and in the United States. The plant grows 1-2 feet tall and its pale green leaves come in three parts, like clover. Near the base of the leaves' long pods shoot out, each containing 10-20 seeds.

Abesh is an intriguing plant that has a multi-faceted, if paradoxical, aspect. Here is a more or less complete list.

1. In the literature, the seeds are described as smelling like maple syrup, celery, or burnt sugar. Yet their taste is bitter and unappealing. Roasting can usually soften the edge of the unpleasant flavor.

2. Abesh can be used as an herb (leaves) or a spice (seeds).

3. The fresh leaves are mild and pleasant, the dried ones are bitter.

4. Abesh has all the characteristic of a legume—it's rich in fiber and protein—but it's treated like a spice.

5. Abesh is probably one of the few spices that contains all four pillars of health—vitamins, minerals, phytonutrients, and fiber.

6. Like many spices and herbs, abesh has a long history of use as both a culinary and medicinal plant since ancient times. It was one of the spices that ancient Egyptians used to embalm mummies and one of the items found in King Tut's tomb. Ancient Greeks and Romans had a less lofty yet practical use for the plant: they fed it to their cattle.

The benefits of abesh

Let's see what abesh hides behind its hard seeds and bitter taste. As I mentioned above, abesh contains a variety of nutrients, phytochemicals, and fiber. It's these constituents that make it beneficial to the body.

Internal benefits

In one human study, abesh was found to lower the bad cholesterol (LDL) and sugar levels in the blood. This study was done with persons who had type-2, non-insulin dependent diabetes. In another controlled, double-blind trial, researchers found that Fenugreek lowered elevated cholesterol and triglyceride levels in patients who had type-1, insulin-dependent diabetes.

Here is list of internal benefits attributed to abesh:

Managing cholesterol Abesh seeds contain alkaloids and steroidal saponins (soap-like substances), which are believed to inhibit cholesterol synthesis and absorption from the digestive tract. The fibers in abesh can help purge excess cholesterol, fat, and sugar as the spice's bulk goes through the GI (gastro-intestinal) tract. It's also been discovered that an amino acid compound called 4-hydroxy isoleucine found in abesh seeds increases the production of insulin in the body. For this reason, abesh is often included in the diet of diabetics. Abesh does not affect the good (HDL) cholesterol.

An associated benefit is that this spice can also help reduce high blood pressure and the risk of heart disease.

Heart burn/acid reflux If you suffer from this condition, soak abesh in warm water overnight then take a teaspoon of it with your meal. The mucilage (water soluble fiber) coats the lining of the stomach, thereby soothing and minimizing the problem.

Manage or lose weight Galactomannan is the name of the soluble fiber found in abesh. This substance, when soaked, absorbs water and swells up. The same thing happens in the GI tract when abesh is consumed, making the person feel full and causing him or her to eat less. This effect should allow a person to lose weight over time.

Good remedy for sore throat Drink a warm solution of abesh, honey, and lemon and this should help sooth your sore throat.

Eliminate excess fat, sugar, and toxins The high mucilage content of abesh should help purge any excessive and harmful substances from the GI tract. For example, 100 grams of abesh seed provides 24.6 grams or 65% of the recommended daily fiber intake.

The non-starch polysaccharides found in abesh include saponins, mucilage, tannin, pectin, and hemicellulose. It's these compounds that remove cholesterol and excess sugar and toxins from the body, thereby protecting the colon from cancer.

For your skin and hair Abesh, when used as a pack and applied on the face and elsewhere on the body, is thought to help lessen blackheads and pimples and reduce lines and wrinkles. You can wash the skin and hair with water that contains abesh soaked overnight. Alternatively, you can use an abesh paste both on the hair and face. Leave it on for 10-15 minutes and then wash off. Abesh boiled in coconut oil, cooled, and applied to the scalp is supposed to help with thinning hair.

For women issues Abesh is known to reduce menstrual discomfort, help induce labor, and increase milk production in lactating women. This spice is also known to increase breast size, help with hot flashes, increase libido, and reduce the vaginal dryness associated with menopause.

For men issues Abesh is a known natural aphrodisiac. It is supposed to increase sexual desire, virility, and performance. The sexual benefits are derived from the phytochemicals found in the abesh seeds, which convert into sex hormones in our bodies. And there are a great number of these chemicals in abesh.

Abesh is a rich source of copper, magnesium, calcium, iron, selenium, zinc, and manganese.

It's also a good source of potassium, which is an antagonistic partner with sodium in the body fluids and helps regulate heart rate and blood pressure. Abesh contains a good number of vitamins, including Vitamin B6, thiamin, folic acid, niacin, riboflavin, Vitamin A, and Vitamin C. These nutrients, along with phyto-chemicals and fiber, work as synergistic Four Pillars partners to keep your body at optimum health.

You can drink ground abesh mixed with water and honey added to taste, or soak the whole seed in water overnight and drink the resulting gelatinous mixture. You can apply a warm poultice (bandage) of the spice over eczema or irritated skin to find relief and sooth the area.

For tea preparation: add 7 tablespoons of abesh seeds to 4 cups of boiling water and let steep for about 20 minutes. Filter, add honey or sugar and drink.

In Ethiopia it's the flour that's commonly used to make a drink. For this purpose, abesh flour is poured slowly onto water and allowed to steep overnight. This prac-tice is to remove the spice's bitterness. In the morning, the liquid is drained care-fully and the residue beaten for several minutes by adding water and sugar or honey alternatively. The resulting beverage is considered very healthy and nourishing and is often drunk during the long fasting days.

I hope the next time you make your abesh drink or use it as a flavoring agent in foods, you keep its many benefits in mind.

Caveat: Abesh can cause the release of a distinct body odor in sweat or urine.

CHAPTER 3
Allspice

Allspice, also called Jamaica pepper, pimento, English pepper, to mention a few of the names it's known by, is from the *Pimenta dioica* tree native to southern Mexico, and Central America. Now it also grows in many countries where the climate is warm. It was named allspice by the English in the early sixteen hundreds because they thought it contained the combined flavor of cloves, cinnamon and nutmeg.

The allspice fruit is picked while it's still green and traditionally dried in the sun. This causes the outer skin to shrivel like prunes. In fact, they resemble the larger version of black pepper when they dry, which also goes through the same process. The leaves are used sometimes as an infusion into sauces, but they are removed before serving. Both the wood and leaves are often used to smoke and impart flavor to meats.

Allspice is a regular ingredient in Caribbean dishes, and in *moles* (pronounced molaye)—a common Mexican cuisine made with red chilies, almond, peanuts, cinnamon and chicken. In India and elsewhere, allspice is also found in curries, in pickled foods, and in the Middle East, in stews and meat dishes. In the United States and many European countries, allspice is mostly found in desserts and commercial sausages.

In Ethiopian cooking, allspice is found in berbere and meklesha (see recipe pages). When ground, allspice does live out its namesake. It gives off the combined aroma of cloves, cinnamon and nutmeg.

Allspice's essential oils—eugenol and a class of compounds called, phenyl-propanoids—have had many medicinal uses. These compounds and others are responsible for the medley of aromas found in allspice. When used as tea, allspice is known to help with excessive gas in the GI tract, and with indigestion problems as well as serving as tonic to the overall health of the body. It's also known to aid with circulation.

This exotic herb of the Americas reportedly brings relief to muscle aches and pains, fights infection and helps normalize blood sugar (important for diabetics). It's also known to have antifungal, anti-microbial and anti-inflammatory proper-ties. As antioxidants, the compounds of allspice may help with heart health, fight cancer and slow the aging of our bodies. Furthermore, in Ayurvedic medicine, allspice is used to treat colds, diarrhea, hysterical paroxysms and fatigue as well as in muscle and joint pains. For tooth aches allspice can have a numbing effect.

Finally, all spice also contains a number of minerals and vitamins, which add to its nutritional value.

CHAPTER 4
Beso Bela (Sacred Basil)

Beso bela was one of the perennial herbs in my mother's garden. It has a beautiful aroma, close to sweet basil, but beso bela is more refined and delicate. Just about every Ethiopian dish worth its salt has to have beso bela—the leaves, flowers, and seeds are used. It's in berbere, mitmita, and is a crucial component of the herbs used to impart aroma and taste to *niter kibbeh*—clarified butter.

Beso bela's stems are often straight and hardy and snap like kindling when you break them. Small, parchment-like pink blossoms grow at discrete points along the top portion of closely grown stems, making them appear like a collection of minarets. The leaves are hairy and grow out of the stems at discreet points, too, like shelves.

In Ethiopia, beso bela is revered for its aroma and flavor but in India, it's venerated for its holiness. Just about every Hindu home has a shrine built outside for the plant and they worship it every morning. They call the plant *Tulsi*—meaning The Incomparable One. This plant symbolizes the goddess Lakshmi, wife of Vishnu, one of India's important deities. Beyond beso bela's association with Hindu's divinity, it has also been esteemed for its power, as one writer puts it, to heal "the body, mind and spirit."

Beso bela's healing properties

In Ayurvedic medicine—a traditional Hindu system of medicinal treatment—beso bela has been used as a remedy for a number of ailments, including the common cold, fevers, respiratory disorders, sore throats, and kidney stones. As part of cough syrup, it helps remove mucus and relieve congestion. Drinking a decoction of the herb with honey and ginger is an effective preparation for bronchitis, asthma, and influenza. Furthermore, this holy herb has been used to heal ulcers and infections of the mouth, skin disorders such as ringworms, dermatitis, and loss of pigment, headaches, stress, sore eyes, and digestive disorders.

While many of these claims come out the traditional practices, modern science has also begun exploring beso bela's health benefits. A number of researchers believe that the herb indeed has great promise. For example, in one study, diabetic rats fed powdered beso bela leaves showed a significant drop in serum sugar as well as triglycerides and the LDL (bad) cholesterol levels, while at the same time substantially increasing the HDL (good) cholesterol level. Whether this result is transferable to human subjects is not known, however.

In another experiment, beso bela was tested for whether it helped to manage stress. In 1991 an animal study was published in the *Indian Journal of Pharmacology* where scientists showed that beso bela does indeed work in managing stress. In fact, it was more effective in treating stress than Asian ginseng and Siberian ginseng—both known remedies for the bodily condition.

A 2011 randomized, double-blind, placebo-controlled study on humans showed that beso bela was found 1.6 times or 39% more effective in the management of stress symptoms compared to the placebo group. And beso bela supplements, according to the study, were tolerated by all patients for the duration of the experiment.

We all experience stress in our lives. In fact, biologically, it's an important and necessary component of life. It causes us to react—to stop and fight or flee in time of danger, or when we're called upon to perform at our best—like studying for an exam or working on a project. There is also the type of stress where what's demanded of us is beyond our ability to cope. It can be an everyday traffic jam, a bad relationship with a boss or significant other, or any other challenge or hardship we might be going through.

When we are stressed, our body produces a number of hormones (cortisol, adrenaline, corticosterone, catecholamines, and others). If you need to flee from danger or your body is called upon to function at its best, these hormones are fine, but when they are released chronically, day after day, they can become toxic to our body. In these kinds of situations, our immune system can be weakened, our blood sugar can be out of whack, our body age faster, and we can become depressed. To cope with the problem, some people may resort to overeating or drinking or using drugs.

Those who practice herbal medicine have identified certain plants that can help the body cope or adapt to stressful situations. One of these plants is beso bela. It is used as a tonic—to enhance the overall health and function of the body, and as an adaptogen—enabling the body to adapt and thrive under physical and emotional stress. The phytochemicals eugenol and caryophyllene found in beso bela help normalize the stress hormone levels in the body and assist the person to cope and thrive in demanding situations. These aromatic essential oils reportedly "elevate both mood and spirit and help combat stress," as one writer put it.

Beso bela contains many phenolic bioflavonoids, carotenoids, vitamin A, and other compounds that fight the oxygen and hydroxyl free radicals (see Appendix A), which are some of the deadliest chemical elements, contributing to the aging of our bodies and making us susceptible to cancer and heart disease.

In addition, beso bela comprises other essential oil compounds that were found to be anti-inflammatory, anti-fungal, anti-viral, and anti-bacterial.

This wonderful plant has vitamins A and C and K, and minerals such as zinc, iron, calcium, iron, and manganese.

The point of all this discussion is for you to realize that spices like beso bela and others you use in food preparations are not just for aroma and flavor. They can have many health benefits as well.

CHAPTER 5
Dimbilal (Coriandor)

Dimbilal, or coriander as it's called in English, is one of the staple spices in Ethiopian cooking. It's one of the spices that make up berbere, shiro, niter kibbeh. Wonderfully aromatic, if you're accustomed to it, ground dimbilal can be added to stews and soups and even used in the making of breads. Although ground dimbilal is now readily available, when I was growing up, my mother always bought the pods and cracked them open to get to the two seeds. She often powdered them and combined them with other ingredients to make berbere.

Nobody knows when dimbilal came to Ethiopia but it's one of the oldest spices, which traces back to 5000 B.C. Its history is rooted in the countries of southern Europe, northern Africa, and southwestern Asia. Dimbilal is mentioned in the Bible and was found in the burial chambers of some of the pharaohs of Egypt. In ancient Greece, it was valued for its medicinal properties as much as for its culinary functions.

For those of us who live in North America, dimbilal has two different names. I'll clarify here for Ethiopians who may not be familiar. The European Spanish term for coriander is cilantro. In North America, however, particularly in Mexico, cilantro generally refers to the leaves. The Mexicans refer to the seed as *semilla* (pronounced, sey-me-ya) *de cilantro*—the seed of cilantro. In the English-speaking world, coriander refers strictly to the seeds.

In ancient cultures (even in some parts of the world at present) dimbilal was valued for its medicinal properties as much as for its benefit in food seasoning. Now modern science has identified the real benefits of dimbilal's volatile oils and aromatic substances.

In January 2011, the *Indian Journal of Experimental Biology* reported that diabetic laboratory animals fed dimbilal powder showed a significant drop in the blood sugar level while there was an increase in the insulin level. The researchers also noted a higher level of antioxidant activity in the tissues of these animals. In research done by Islamic Azad University of Iran and published in the March 2009 issue of *Phytotherapy Research*, lab animals fed dimbilal seed extract showed a drop in blood sugar and increased levels of insulin production. Although we cannot say that these findings apply to humans as well, the fact that these researchers found a definite correlation between the consumption of dimbilal seeds and a drop in blood sugar is a good indication that humans can potentially benefit from including dimbilal in their diet.

Dimbilal also reduced the bad cholesterol and triglyceride levels in the blood, which means regular consumption of this spice, can potentially help with the health of the heart and the blood vessels. Additionally, Dimbilal was found to sooth inflammations, and to improve the health of the nervous system and the digestive tract. Dimbilal's antioxidant compounds are also believed to help with the health of the eyes, particularly with conjunctivitis (pink eye) and macular degeneration.

Traditionally, dimbilal has likewise been used to treat nausea, seasonal fever, stomach problems, vomiting, bed cold, rheumatism, and joint pain. Dimbilal seed oil has been used as an analgesic (substance that relieves pain) and for its fungicidal and anti-bacterial properties, as a deodorant, and even as an aphrodisiac. Speaking of dimbilal's antibacterial property, it is supposed to be one of the better natural treatments for Salmonella poisoning, and for diarrhea caused by fungal infection.

All these benefits come from dimbilal's many essential volatile oils and antioxidant compounds. Its leaves can be good natural cleansing agents as well.

Dimbilal's leaves and seeds are good sources of vitamins and minerals, fiber (especially the leaves), and phytonutrients. A bunch of home-grown dimbilal leaves can reportedly offer 225% and 258% of the daily allowances of Vitamin A and Vitamin K , respectively. Regarding minerals, dimbilal contains good amounts of potassium, calcium, manganese, iron, and magnesium.

For some of the benefits mentioned above, you can blend dimbilal leaves and/or seeds in water and drink or boil them in water and drink as tea. We blend ours along with the Four Pillar fruits and vegetables. The rich flavor, aroma, and nutrients found in dimbilal can help you to lead a healthy and happy life. How about this: if you can go along with the Chinese belief, dimbilal may even endow you with immortality.

Bon appetit!

CHAPTER 6
Inslal (Anise)

Inslal was the other herb in my mother's garden. She used the delicate green branches and fuzzy, cattail-like leaves mostly to enhance the flavor/aroma of *areqey*—homemade vodka. She also boiled the leaves in water to drink as tea to lessen the effect of a cold. I think she also added a small amount inslal seeds in some of her bread recipes as well as in her stews.

Outside of Ethiopia, anise traditionally has been used as a remedy for asthma, bronchitis, cold-related congestion of the chest and throat, and disorders of the digestive tract, such as bloating, flatulence, nausea, and dyspepsia.

Anise has moreover been used to stimulate appetite and promote digestion. The herb does this by stimulating the production of enzymes and digestive juices. To take advantage this herb's benefits, people customarily chew anise seeds, drink hot anise tea, and eat appetizers or desserts made with anise seeds.

Anise's essential oils have both sedative (in high doses) and stimulatory (in low doses) effects. This dose-dependent property of the herb's oils has found uses in the treatment of epileptic and hysteric attacks, and by those who suffer from spells of anxiety, anger, and insomnia. Anise can have a tranquilizing effect on these persons. Those who are in low spirits for whatever reason can be helped if they take a concentrated anise tea or drink water containing two or three drops of the herb's essential oils. Anise can similarly improve circulation and increase blood flow in the remote tissues. This means that people who are diabetic, rheumatic, and arthritic can find relief by increased blood circulation.

Anise has also been used as diuretic, allowing the body to remove toxins and fluid build-up from the tissues.

Additionally, this sweet and fragrant herb has had varied uses by women: to increase milk production and flow while nursing, to kick-start menstruation, to alleviate the pain and discomfort associated with menstruation, and as an aphrodisiac.

The essential oils in anise have antibacterial, antispasmodic, and purgative properties. This means if you have wounds, scabies, or even lice, drops of the herb's oils can protect the affected areas and speed up their healing. If you have excessive contraction of the respiratory tract, blood vessels, nerves, muscles, or even internal organs that turn into cramps and convulsions and similar symptoms, anise oil can be a good palliative and anti-spasmodic agent for these conditions.

Anise oil's purgative or carminative benefits come from the herb's ability to minimize bloating and remove gas from the GI tract. For those who suffer from pain and cramps associated with excessive gas build-up, an herbal remedy like anise seeds can be a welcome source of relief.

Anise seeds contain a number of phytochemicals, predominant among which is anethole, a volatile essential oil that gives anise its aroma and flavor. The seeds are also rich in B-complex vitamins and a great many minerals. From reading the earlier chapters you know how important these nutrients are to the body's proper day-to-day functioning as well as long-term health. Herbs and spices are important sources of these key components of wellness.

Anise has traditionally been used, in many different cultures, to flavor various dishes and alcoholic beverages. Anise is found in Anisette (most Mediterranean countries), Arak (the traditional alcoholic beverage of many Middle Eastern countries), Raki (Turkey), Ouzo (Greece), Mastika (Balkans), Patis (France), Absinthe (originally from Switzerland, but now available throughout Europe), Sambuca (Italy), Xtabentún (Mexico), and others.

Nowadays, anise is also used in dairy products, candies, meats, and gelatins. It's likewise used in creams, soaps, perfumes, and sachets.

Do you want to have fresh and pleasant breath? Chew a few anise seeds before you go out.

To get anise's many benefits, boil 2-3 tablespoons of the seeds in 3 cups of water for 3 minutes. Let it cool and then blend. Filter the liquid with a fine mesh sieve or cheesecloth, and serve with ice cubes. Alternatively, you can also consume it as a hot drink. You can be creative with anise seeds. People often add it to breads, soups, sauces, cookies, and other foods. We do, too.

Anise's other benefits: A cloth soaked in a tincture of anise can be used as a compress to sooth the eyes, to treat scabies, psoriasis and lice.

Caveat: very high doses of anise oil can slow down circulation and respiration, and can cause vomiting, pulmonary edema, and seizures. Anise can be poisonous to small animals and even to children in high amounts. Pregnant women should not consume excessive levels of the herb. Anise can cause an allergic reaction to skin and some internal organs such as the respiratory and GI tracts.

CHAPTER 7
Ird (Turmeric)

This pile of golden flour (for those who are reading this book with color digital devices) doesn't come from dried and powdered Maskel daisies, the fruit of mangos or papaws, or from bell peppers of the same hue. The sun has no direct hand in its creation, unlike all the other colorful phytonutrients synthesized in leaves and petals or within the flesh of fruits and vegetables. It comes from the turmeric plant's finger-like underground stems (shown above), which are similar in growth to ginger, kratchai, and glangal.

Turmeric (also known as *curcuma longa*) is a spice native to India, where it's been used for 4000 years, as a condiment and medicine, and for certain ceremonial events. Now turmeric is widely grown in nearly all Southeast Asian countries and other tropical places. Its uses—both as spice and medicine—have been exported to other countries over the past several centuries.

Turmeric was introduced to China around 700 A.D., to Ethiopia and the rest of eastern Africa around 800 A.D., and from the 1200s A.D onward to eastern Africa and Europe.

Traditionally, in India, China, and most other Asian countries, turmeric is used as a food flavoring and color agent, as a dye for fabrics, and as medicine to treat the body for a number of ailments and diseases.

Curry, the most famous of the Indian spices, is partly turmeric—it imparts the deep orange color and heady smell to the condiment. The other components are ground coriander, cumin, abesh (fenugreek), ginger, mustard, cinnamon, and black pepper. In many of these countries, turmeric also has much religious and cultural significance.

In Hinduism, turmeric powder is a symbol of purity of mind and spirit as well as one's inner pride and security. For many, the herb also signifies fertility, prosperity, chastity, and sensuality. For all these reasons, worshipers often anoint their sacred images with turmeric paste.

Similarly, in Buddhism, yellow is tied to generosity, prosperity, and purity—this is the reason Buddhist monks wear robes dyed deep orange. Because of turmeric's association with fertility and good luck, Hindus and Buddhists use it in religious and wedding ceremonies.

Equally significant is turmeric's long-time use to treat and heal the body. Traditionally, turmeric has been used to relieve arthritis, dissolve gallstones, treat bloating, and as tonic to improve the overall health of the body. Furthermore, turmeric has been used to alleviate or heal asthma, allergies, rheumatism, diabetic wounds, runny nose, cough, and sinusitis.

In many Asian countries, turmeric is used as a disinfectant for burns, cuts, and bruises. When applied as a paste, turmeric can be effective in treating these conditions and in enhancing the appearance of the skin. Many cosmetics companies now use turmeric in the manufacture of their products.

The science behind the traditional uses of turmeric

Out of its traditional uses came the discovery that turmeric indeed has many healthful properties. Hundreds of research studies have been done on the benefit of turmeric to human health. In test tube studies and lab animal models as well as on humans, turmeric has been found to treat chronic inflammation of the colon or large intestine (a condition known as ulcerative colitis), chronic disease of the air passages, asthma, and rheumatoid arthritis, to name but just a few.

In other studies, turmeric was found to help fight cancer of the colon, skin, pancreas, blood (childhood leukemia), and liver. Similarly, there have been studies documenting the benefit of the spice on psoriasis, Alzheimer's disease, arthritis, and even depression. These findings have not been without controversy, however. Because some of the experiments were in test tube and animal models, there are those who suggest that what worked in a lab and in animals may not work when applied to human subjects.

What contributes to turmeric's beneficial properties?

So far, more than 100 compounds have been isolated from turmeric, including the main coloring agents, volatile oils known as turmerone and curcuminoids. Of all these, curcumin is the most studied. Turmeric's anti-cancer property comes largely from this chemical and its relatives' antioxidants. As you may have read earlier in the book (more in Appendix A), antioxidants help neutralize free radicals, which are believed to be one of the main causes of cancers. The other antioxidants found in Turmeric are vitamins C and E and several carotenoids.

Curcumin moreover has the capacity to neutralize cancer-causing substances and in stopping mutated cells from turning cancerous. This compound is good for the heart. As an antiviral, curcumin can help speed up the healing of wounds.

How to use turmeric

In Ethiopia turmeric is used to color foods and as a part of spice blends. You can increase your intake of turmeric by adding it to meat stews and even shiro wot.

I'll leave it up to your ingenuity to determine how much of the spice you want to add to the different dishes. The key is to make sure that the additional turmeric doesn't lessen or exaggerate the flavor of the other ingredients. You can add turmeric to rice, lentils, *nifro* (a cooked mixture of wheat berries and legumes), egg salad, and other dishes that don't already have spices in them. One writer recommends adding turmeric to sautéed apples, steamed cauliflower, and green beans and onions. She also suggests mixing brown rice with raisins and cashews and seasoning them with turmeric, cumin, and coriander.

Turmeric has no known toxicity.

Enjoy!

CHAPTER 8
Kewrerima (False Cardamom)

Kewrerima is one of our prized spices. Its aroma is rich and beguiling, and for those who are used to Ethiopian foods, mouth-watering. Kewrerima is found in just about every base spice blend, including berbere, mitmita, niter kibbeh, and other mixes constituted to create elaborate or rare dishes. Kewrerima is sometimes used to flavor and give an extra kick to the aroma of freshly made coffee and tea.

What's in a name?

Ethiopians who know this wonderful spice as kewrerima may be confused when they notice the English name. They might even be a little taken aback. Why would someone call one of their favorite spices *false* cardamom—an imposter? Incidentally, it's also called Ethiopian cardamom, which would be more fitting, but it's not widely known by this moniker. The distinction in name actually started during ancient Roman and Greek times, when spices began to come from India. I'll explain this in just a bit.

The various cardamoms that exist in the world today belong to the ginger family, *Zingiberaceae*. There are two genera in this family, to use a biology term. One is *Elettaria*, consisting of the smaller straw green pods, called green cardamom or *true* cardamom.

A native of southwest India, green cardamom also grows in Guatemala, Sri Lanka, Malaysia, Thailand, Tanzania, and in a few other tropical countries. India, Guatemala, and Sri Lanka are, respectively the number 1, 2, and 3 producers and exporters of green cardamom.

The Middle East, the Scandinavian countries, and India itself are the greatest consumers of green cardamom. This spice is the third most expensive in the world of spices, after saffron and vanilla, because cardamom's crop yield is so low—only 40 to 120 pounds per acre. Comparatively, 2,000 pounds of caraway seeds can be harvested in a similar acreage.

With its long luxuriant leaves and reedy stems, green, or true, cardamom grows in clumps like bamboo to a height of 10 to 15 feet. The production is labor intensive, as it needs constant care and the pods have to be picked individually by hand. (See next page for more info.)

The second type of cardamom is called *amomum*. It has a larger pod and comes in shades of black, dark brown, red, and white, and has many different regional names. Amomum grows mainly in Asia, Africa, and Australia.

The "true" and "false" names assigned to the cardamoms were supposedly coined by a 4th century B.C. Greek botanist named Theophrastus, who had been given conflicting information as to the sources of the two varieties. One of his sources said they came from the land of Mendes, in northern Persia. A second said they came from India. Hence, he named the green kind *true* cardamom, and the others *false* cardamom.

To further complicate matters, the amomum genus has hundreds of species, one of which is *aframomum*, which is kewrerima or Ethiopian cardamom. Kewrerima grows in western Ethiopia (around Lake Tana), in southern Sudan, and in Uganda. As most of you know and I mentioned above, kewrerima is one of the major ingredients in berbere, mekelesha, mitten shiro and mitmita. Unfortunately, there has not been much compositional analysis done on kewrerima (that I could find) to determine the level of vitamins and minerals and the diverse phytonutrients and volatile oils it comprises.

The western African species is known as *Aframomum melegueta* but its everyday name is alligator pepper or grains of paradise. Its seeds are hotter than the Ethiopian variety. A Japanese study found that grains of paradise can lower body fat and decrease waist to hip ratio. Besides its culinary uses, this spice has also been esteemed as an aphrodisiac.

CHAPTER 9
Cardamom

Green and brown cardamom

Green cardamom is one of the four key ingredients in the freshly made Ethiopian tea. The others are cinnamon, cloves and black tea but it is the third member that the ancient Silk Road traders once called the Queen of Spices that gives the tea its distinct and luscious flavor. Drinking this tea can be as pleasurable an experience as drinking coffee produced in certain regions of Ethiopia; it is that rich, smooth and savory hot beverage we all enjoy so much. I've covered cloves and cinnamon in the spices section of this book. Let's talk about the green cardamom in detail and some basic information about one of the Asian amomum cardamoms.

Green Cardamom's nutritional profile and benefits

All cardamoms have been valued for both their culinary and medicinal benefits. In western countries the green cardamom has been esteemed more than others because of its distinct bouquet and flavor—intensely aromatic, but not pungent or spicy tangy, yet warm and tasty. And somehow, like fine prose or poetry, green cardamom appears to contain layers of flavor and aroma, each fine and delicate. Because of these qualities, green cardamom has versatile application in savory dishes.

In India and the Arab countries green cardamom is used in various sweets, teas and coffees as well as spice mixes like curry and Garam Masala—a blend used in rice dishes and snacks. In the United States, green cardamom is often used in flans, soups, stews, purees, and rice dishes, as well as ice creams and fresh fruit salad. Scandinavian countries use ground cardamom in baked foods such as breads, buns, biscuits, and cakes, as well as in meatballs.

The brown or black cardamoms are bigger in size and have a different aroma and flavor than their smaller green cousins. They give off a smoky fragrance with a slightly mint and pepper overtone. Some have described their aroma as camphor-like. The seeds are somewhat sweetish and not as strongly pungent as the green ones. In India, they are used in several spice mixes and flavorsome dishes—ranging from curries to stews, lentil dishes and pilafs. They can also be found in rice pudding, tea and even coffee beverages. Historically black and brown cardamoms have also been employed to treat various stomach ailments, common infections and dental problems.

True Cardamom can help with digestive disorders (bloating, acidity, heartburn, nausea, and constipation). It has diuretic properties and, therefore, can aid in removing toxins and other bodily waste efficiently. In time-honored Ayurvedic medicine, cardamom is used to fight depression and bad breath. It's similarly known to help with infection of the mouth and throat.

Spicy drinks are great to drive away the common cold and flu. Cardamom with kundo berbere (black pepper) and turmeric can do the trick. I often also add, pinches of rosemary, anise and a tablespoon full of honey and lemon for this purpose.

The phytochemicals in cardamom work as an antioxidants and anti-inflammatory. In some studies, these compounds have been found to inhibit the growth of cancer cells, bacteria and fungus. Cardamom is also good at keeping the platelets in the blood fully dispersed. It's anti-spasmodic, meaning it can help with muscle and gastro-intestinal cramps as well as hiccups.

Additionally, green cardamom houses a range of minerals consisting of calcium, magnesium, manganese, copper, iron, phosphorous and zinc. The manganese content is astounding. In a hundred grams of the green cardamom, there are 28 mg or 1,217% of the daily value of the mineral. Manganese is involved in many enzyme reactions, including those that fight free radicals in the body and help minimize the incidence of cancer and heart diseases. Lastly, cardamom contains a fair amount of vitamins, including, pyridoxine, riboflavin, niacin and Vitamin C.

Now you can see why those ancient Silk Road merchants crowned it "the queen of spices," just as they had bestowed black pepper as the King of Spices. The next time you sit down to eat your Ethiopian food or drink tea or your Four Pillar hot beverage constituted with cardamom seeds and other spices, you should think of all the good things they bring to your health and wellness.

Enjoy!

CHAPTER 10
Koseret *(Lippia Javanica)*

Koseret is one of the spices that impart aroma and good taste to Ethiopian clarified butter. It's also used in many spice blends, including berbere, mitmita and mitten shiro. In the countryside, farmers often feed their cattle koseret leaves because the herb reportedly makes their meat tender and flavorful.

Botanically, koseret or lippia javanica belongs to *verbenaceae* family. Koseret is one of 200 species distributed throughout tropical and southern Africa, eastern India, and South and Central America. It grows 3 to 6 feet high, with large aromatic leaves and white flowers. Koseret mostly grows in the wild. It is sometimes cultivated and grown in private home gardens—both for aesthetics and its aroma as well as for its culinary and medicinal values.

Wherever it grows in the world, the locals have their own name for the plant, just as Ethiopians do. In English, koseret is known as lemon bush or fever tea. Its botanical name, *lippia javanica*, however, has a bit of history. The first part of the name, lippia, was given by the French physician and natural historian, Augustin Lippi (1678-1705) who was sent by Louis XIV as part of a delegation to start trade relations with Ethiopia. The second part, javanica, was given by a German botanist called Nicolaas Laurens Burman (1734-1793), who believed that the plant came from Java.

Medical uses of koseret

It is reported that some tribal groups in southern Africa use a tea of koseret leaves and stems to treat coughs, colds, and fevers. A poultice of the plant extract is employed to treat skin conditions such as scabies and scalp infection. The smoke of the dry plant is supposed to alleviate asthma and chronic cough and chest congestion. Koseret is used to kill insects, lice and mites and provides protection against mosquitos.

To ascertain traditional claims, modern researchers have done experiments with lab animals and human subjects and have demonstrated that koseret has undeniable anti-inflammatory, anti-microbial and decongestant properties. Koseret is an effective repellant against mosquitoes and insects.

Outside of Ethiopia, koseret's culinary use is very limited. Some cultures use the lemon bush oil extract as flavoring agent, or add the dried leaves to fresh fruit and cooked dishes.

CHAPTER 11
Kundo Berbere (Black Pepper)

Kundo berbere or black pepper is one of the oldest and widely used spices in the world— so much so that it's often referred to as the King of All Spices. During the Middle Ages kundo berbere was used as currency. People paid rent, dowries, and taxes with black pepper seeds. It's no wonder it used to be called "black gold."

Kundo berbere originated in southern India and Sri Lanka, and it is now grown in countries such as Indonesia, Malaysia, Vietnam, Brazil, China and Thailand. Kundo berbere comes from a climbing vine called piper nigrum, one of a thousand varieties of a larger plant family called *piperaceae*. The plant can grow up to 30 feet high. It produces round berries that turn red upon full ripening.

The kundo berbere we consume is generally picked when the berries are still green. Then it is dried under the sun, which causes them to shrink and shrivel like prunes. The white kundo berbere comes from the same plant but a mechanical or chemical process is used to remove the outer skin of the berries. White pepper tastes milder and is used in light colored dishes and condiments such as soufflés, white sauces and mayonnaise.

No definitive record exists to show when kundo berbere came to Ethiopia. Historians, such as the famed Richard Pankhurst says it might have come during the height of the Axumite era, around the first century A.D., when Ethiopia was a powerful trading partner with India. But if the spice had such an ancient introduction into the country, why was it not widely used? According to reports, as recently as Emperor Lebna Dingle's rule (1508-1540 A.D.) kundo berbere was available only to the royal household.

No matter, this gentle and zesty spice has had a much longer foothold in Ethiopian soil than the red or cayenne pepper, introduced into the country in the 18th century. Cayenne pepper and its relatives claim South and Central America as their historical home. In Ethiopian cooking, kundo berbere is used mostly by itself or as part of the mekelesha in stews and soups that need extra gentle heat and flavor.

Just as important, if not more so, is kundo berbere's benefit to the human body. Kundo berbere contains a number of phytonutrients that define its characteristics—odor, color, heat, and aroma—and its health benefits.

Kundo berbere contains essential oils, flavonoids, lignans, alkaloids, aromatic compounds and amids. Compounds called chavicine and piperine are responsible for kundo berbere's spice and flavor.

In the vitamin area, kundo berbere contains choline, folic acid, niacin, pyridoxine, riboflavin, thiamin, vitamin A, Vitamin C and Vitamin K.

Mineral-wise, calcium, copper, iron, magnesium, manganese, phosphorus, and zinc are the main ones found in The King of All Spices.

Kundo berbere's health benefits

Based on research findings as well as traditional uses, the literature accounts quite extensive health benefits to this spice, which occupies our kitchen cabinets unsung and unadmired. We use the spice on a whim or when compelled to use kundo berbere and others spices in a special dish.

Kundo berbere can enhance appetite, clean out chest congestion, speed up recovery from a cold, heal sore throats, help with fever, improve digestion and calmly normalize a malfunctioning GI tract. Piperine, one of the phytonutrients found in kundo berbere, is the compound responsible for all of these benefits. Black pepper can also help with conditions associated with stomach pain, chills, blood poisoning, intestinal gas (bloating), nausea, strep throat, headache, hypothermia-induced vomiting, malaria, dysentery, cholera and even arthritis.

Black pepper improves circulation, kills a wide spectrum of microbes, alleviates pain, and calms and sooths inflamed tissues and organs. As you will see be-low, kundo berbere has a wide range of anti-cancer properties. The compounds in kundo berbere have been found to be superior antioxidants in neutralizing free radicals and protecting the body from carcinogenic substances.

Applied externally, a mixture of black pepper powder and cream and oil, can help ease problems associated with nasal congestion, skin eruptions, sinusitis and epilepsy. Because kundo berbere has antibacterial properties, it can be used as a food preservative.

Bioavailability

The compounds found in kundo berbere have other unique properties; they can increase the absorption, assimilation and function of foods in our bodies. Piperine not only increases the bioavailability of other phytonutrients to the body but also boosts their activity once they are in the tissues. Piperine does this by enhancing the phytonutrient's absorption across the intestinal wall. Once they are absorbed into the blood stream, piperine can protect them against oxidative damage until finally they get into the cells where they are needed to do their own protective work. The function of this ancient spice is truly remarkable!

By including black pepper with your meals often, you can increase the effica-cy of the phytonutrients in the food you consume as well as benefit from kundo berbere's own antioxidants. This is the reason you see black pepper in all the Four Pillars recipes. The piperine enables active compounds from other foods to stay in the body's cells longer. Researchers who found this correlation applied piperine and curcumin (the compound found in turmeric) to both animal and human models. They concluded that piperine increased curcumin's absorption, its serum concentration and bioavailability.

We often add extra kundo berbere to our glass of Four Pillars drink. It gives character, zest and heat to the beverage.

Cancer prevention

By increasing the availability of other cancer-fighting phytonutrients and using its own antioxidant compounds, black pepper can help minimize the incidence of cancer and the aging of our bodies. Piperine also thwarts communication between existing cancer cells, thereby limiting their growth and proliferation.

Additionally, by stimulating the production of the body's specialized enzymes, black pepper can help neutralize and eliminate cancer-causing chemicals from the body. Rancidity, caused by the oxidation of fats and cholesterol, is a common problem with fats—both within and outside the body. It is generally a result of a free radical attack on fat and cholesterol molecules. The black pepper compounds can serve as effective natural antioxidants and as a food preservative. So perhaps the next time you plan to store your meat you may want to treat it with black pepper powder first.

Black pepper's other benefits

Black pepper can serve as an anti-inflammatory for those who suffer from rheumatoid arthritis, inflammation of the bronchioles of the lungs, inflammation of the stomach lining, and a great many similar problems.

Black pepper may help improve brain health, particularly in those who are suffering from reduced memory, cognitive malfunction, Alzheimer's disease, dementia or other age-related brain conditions.

Black pepper can help lower cholesterol by increasing the breakdown and utilization of fats in the body. This King of All Spices can also help boost the immune system and treat problems with intermittent fever such as those induced by malaria, colds, and neuritis. Black pepper can assist with the efficient digestion and processing of foods by stimulating the taste buds and increasing the secretion of digestive juices in the stomach. As you can see, kundo berbere indeed is a remarkable spice, fitting of its royal status.

Medicinal uses of black pepper

Include this great spice with your daily meals as a general protection of your health. You may want to take a concentrated amount. Grind the berries, boil them in water and drink the decoction. I generally add a teaspoon of turmeric, the juice from a slice of lemon and honey to taste. You'll feel great afterwards.

Caveat and disclaimer: Avoid excessive topical application of black pepper, as it can stimulate the kidneys. Pregnant women should not take concentrated amounts of black pepper—the pungent compounds can cause burns to the fetus.

Finally, by all means, don't treat kundo berbere/black pepper as medicine, although it does have medicinal properties. Consult with your physician if you have health problems or are on medication before including the spice as part of your daily nutrition.

Enjoy!

CHAPTER 12
Mitmita (Bird's Eye Chili)

It's hard to believe that the peppers grown and used as part of our berbere or mitmita are not native to Ethiopia. According to reports, all the peppers used around the world today originated in the Americas—Mexico, Central America, and South America. Although some say Columbus, who discovered America, might have brought chili peppers to Europe even earlier, it was the Spanish and Portuguese traders who introduced the peppers to the rest of the world in the 16th and 17th centuries. Tomatoes, corn (or maize), pineapple and potatoes came from the Americas, too.

How did Ethiopians survive up to that time without their precious peppers? For that matter, how did the rest of the world survive, depending on peppers for so many different cuisines?

I have no answers, except to say that people made use of whatever herbs they had, like watercress in the case of Ethiopia. Long before computers were introduced, we depended on the typewriter. Long before cars and airplanes came into existence, we depended on horses, carriages and our feet to get to and from places. Now, it seems hard to believe that humans once existed without all these conveniences.

I guess the same goes for our wonderful herbs and spices that have been spread around the world from their places of origin. We need to share what we've got with the rest of the world. East Indians are the purveyors of many of spices we use today. In a limited way, I guess the rest of the world might say the same about coffee and probably in years to come about teff, too. Coffee and teff are Ethiopia's gift to the world.

Mitmita, or bird's eye chili to use its English name, is one of the hottest peppers from Ethiopia. Outside their native land, there are several other peppers a lot hotter than mitmita, so much so that people have to wear masks and suits when they pick them.

To clarify, mitmita refers both to the bird's eye chili pepper and to a powdered seasoning mix that usually contains, in addition to the chili, cardamom, cloves and salt. Some people enrich it by adding ginger, cinnamon, cumin and other ingredients to increase mitmita's range of use.

The final mixture varies from bright to dark orange, depending on the number and kind of spices that have been included along with the base four (cardamom, cloves, salt and chili). Its aroma and flavor also change from formulation to formulation. No matter what it has in it, mitmita is still fiery hot.

Beyond aroma, flavor and spiciness, let's talk about the benefit of mitmita to your health. This discussion refers just to the chili itself.

The benefits of mitmita

First of all, remember that almost all peppers go from green to red if left on the vine. When peppers become red, it means they are rich in phytonutrients—carotenoids, bioflavonoids and vitamins. Red pepper has 8 times more Vitamin A than green pepper. Their beta -carotene content is significantly greater too, going from −137% of DV in green pepper to 841% of DV in red.

Capsaicin is the compound that gives peppers their fiery taste. It is an odor-less, colorless and oily chemical. The "heat" in capsaicin that we feel on our tongue or when it comes in contact with our skin is more apparent than real. There is no actual physical damage but the chemical tricks the brain into believing that the tissue is being burned. The brain responds by releasing endorphins to relieve the pain and also give the body an overall euphoric feeling. The side effect of this is that when endorphins are floating in your system, your desire to eat is suppressed. For those who are trying to lose or manage weight, these cascading events will cause the person to eat less.

Here are some of the other advantages of capsaicin

Capsaicin can stimulate cells along the lining of your stomach to produce more digestive juice, which means this compound can speed up the breakdown and processing of foods. It's an anti-inflammatory—important for those who have joint problems or tenderness in their nasal cavity or elsewhere in their bodies. The beta-carotene and flavonoids found in chili and all other red peppers can be good antioxidants, neutralizing tissue-damaging free radicals and shielding our genetic material.

Additionally, chili peppers have been found to reduce bad cholesterol, which means that if you're a regular consumer of chili peppers, you can keep your heart and vascular system healthy. Because of the antioxidant properties of the compounds found in chili and other peppers, studies have shown that these red phytonutrients can potentially help in treating lung and prostate cancer.

When you consume chili peppers, your body's metabolism is enhanced. This is more good news for those who are trying to lose or manage their weight. Chili has been found to help with arthritis and even as an insect repellant and sleep aid. Researchers in Australia reported that those who consumed spicy food before they went to bed slept well, longer, and felt completely rested when they woke. The study also found that these people had more energy and felt more awake. This benefit of chili is probably connected to the incidental release of endorphins, induced by capsaicin, which relaxes and calms the body.

Chilies are good in fighting congestion of the chest and blocked nose, relieving chronic joint and muscle pain and, according a Duke University study, can kill cancer-causing bacteria known as *H. pylori*. Chilies can help prevent the microbial contamination of food, an important advantage in countries where people have no refrigerators.

Those who consume the berbere and powdered mitmita blend can also benefit from the many other spices found in them. See berbere and mitmita's ingredient list under the Ethiopian recipes.

In short, I hope that when you think of chilies and other spices, you will think of their health benefits, in addition to their importance to enhance the flavor, aroma, and taste of your foods.

Bona appetit!

CHAPTER 13
Netch Azmud (Bishop's Weed aka Ajwain)

If you're like me, you probably thought *netch azmud* (also called bishop's weed or ajwain) and *tikur azmud* are related, a variation of each other. One is netch (white), the other tikur (black). As you will see below, they are not related at all, although in some of the Ethiopian dishes they can be used interchangeably.

Ethiopians who cook with these spices know how they taste and smell. For those who are not familiar with these spices, here is the difference.

Some nutrition writers describe netch azmud as having a thyme-like aroma with a cumin undertone. Tikur azmud's whole seed aroma is subtle at the first whiff but becomes pungent when you pulverize them. Aroma, like taste, is an individual thing. Some writers refer to tikur azmud as having a bitter aroma. I think this herb smells rather pleasant, particularly in baked bread but even when the seeds are chewed alone.

Tikur azmud is a native of India. Netch azmud has Ethiopia as one of its homes. It supposedly originated in Egypt and spread to northern Africa, the Middle East, India, and southeastern Asia.

The health benefits of the spice were never thought about because most Ethiopians, like people everywhere else, think of spices and herbs merely as devices to make foods flavorful and enjoyable. What happens to these spices and herbs once they enter the body—whether or not they have any benefits to their health—is never a consideration.

Netch azmud's benefits

Traditionally, the seeds of netch azmud have been used to treat ailments associated with the digestive tract, such as bloating, indigestion, gastrosis, diarrhea, and cholera. This spice has similarly been used for conditions related to the respiratory system, such as asthma, chest pain (angina), common cold, bronchitis, pneumonia and emphysema.

Netch azmud is known to be anti-inflammatory, anti-parasitic, anti-spasmodic, diuretic, and even aphrodisiac. According to one report, a combination of netch azmud, fennel seeds, dried ginger, and salt increases appetite and enhances digestion.

Additionally, a poultice of netch azmud over psoriasis and vitiligo (a chronic disease where the skin loses its pigmentation) can bring relief and healing. Methoxsalen is a prescription drug used to treat psoriasis. It was once made from netch azmud, until the synthetic version took over.

Finally, netch azmud is thought to be an excellent tonic spice, improving the body's overall health.

CHAPTER 14
Netch Shinkoort (Garlic)

Netch shinkoort is the king in Ethiopian cooking. It's a major ingredient in berbere and mitten shiro. Ground garlic and black pepper are combined and powdered and used as finishing touches to sega (meat), doro, and lentil wots (stews). You sprinkle a teaspoonful of it for ten or so minutes before you remove the pot from the fire. Alternatively, you can use mekelesha (see the recipes section.) Again, like all the spices and herbs, garlic's role in Ethiopian dishes is mainly to enhance flavor, taste, character and depth to the foods. Like others, most people don't make a conscious association between the consumption of garlic and its benefit to health and well-being. Let's see what garlic can do for you.

One, garlic contains a group of phytochemicals called organo-sulfur compounds which give the spice both its color and smell. Although modern researchers don't exactly know how these compounds work in the human body, there have been a good number of laboratory and epidemiological studies to show that consuming garlic regularly may be beneficial to our health.

Two, garlic has been valued for its culinary as well medicinal properties since ancient times in many different cultures. Researchers from around the world have identified many of garlic's unique characteristics and benefits to the human body.

Garlic and its sulfur compounds have been found to help control cholesterol production in the body. In a laboratory study, these compounds have also been shown to have blood-thinning properties, one of garlic's traditionally known attributes. Garlic's phytochemicals have been found to promote the health and function of the blood vessels, by making them more supple and pliable. These phytochemicals also have an anti-inflammatory function, important to those who suffer from joint aches and pains. They do this by inhibiting the activities of the enzymes responsible for the condition in the circulating fluids. For those who are concerned about their heart, vascular and circulatory health, regular consumption of garlic can be a benefit.

Garlic compounds have been shown to have antioxidant activity in laboratory tests and some researchers think that it may play the same role in the body. These substances are believed to stimulate the production of glutathione, the body's natural antioxidant and help boost the immune system.

Furthermore, garlic's compounds are believed to disrupt the replication of cancer cells, while at the same time increase their apoptosis or death. In some case-controlled studies, in countries where people consume a higher amount of garlic in their diet had a significantly lower incidence of gastric cancer than those who consume little or none. In a similar study, researchers found that those who have a high intake of garlic in their diets had far less incidence of colorectal cancer than the control group.

Garlic has antibacterial and anti-fungal properties as well. Those who suffer from ring worms of the body and feet can benefit if they use a garlic solution on their skin or soak their feet in it.

A few practical details

Allicin is a key active ingredient in garlic. When you crash garlic you release the enzyme that catalyzes the production of Allicin. Allicin, in turn, rapidly changes into organo-sulfur compounds, some of which are the volatile oils that permeate the air and enter your nostrils.

Cooking reportedly makes the enzyme inactive. It is therefore recommended to let the crashed garlic sit for 10 minutes or more before you cook it. That way, the allicin-producing enzymes would have run through their courses. If your food ingredient calls for garlic, add it near the completion of the cooking. It's also said that if you added garlic toward the end of the cooking, the heat will impact the enzymes less. And never use a microwave oven with all fruits, vegetables and spices. (Microwave ovens use radio waves to agitate and vibrate water molecules in food. As these molecules continue to vibrate and shake they generate heat at atomic level. It's this heat that cooks the food. My concern is when you disturb molecules like this, there is a chance of breaking the bonds and creating free radicals.)

In Ethiopian cooking, the berbere spice blend contains the most amount of garlic. The garlic we find in berbere comes from the crushed, dried and powdered garlic. It has minimal direct heat exposure. So, technically the organo-sulfur compounds of garlic in berbere should be relatively intact.

Then from the comparative case studies done in other countries, those who eat garlic regularly had a low incidence of certain type of cancers than others. You can still benefit even from cooked garlic.

As you will see later, many of the spices found in the Ethiopian cooking have antioxidant and anti-cancer characteristics. The combined effect of the spices found in the stews and the vegetarian and meat dishes should be a benefit to you.

Caveat

Garlic naturally has a strong odor, which can be noticed on one's breath and sweat. It can be offensive if the person doesn't keep good hygiene—take a regular bath, brush and wash their mouth and freshen their breath before coming in contact with people. If too much garlic is consumed, the person could experience heartburn, nausea, flatulence, abdominal pain and diarrhea. Prolonged exposure of garlic to one's skin can cause blisters, contact dermatitis and lesions.

CHAPTER 15
Senafich (Mustard Seeds)

Ground mustard seeds are one of the most common spices in Ethiopian cooking. Their uses vary according to the creativity and imagination of the person using them. The most common use, however, is a dip prepared with vinegar, salt, and garlic. Ground mustard seeds are also one of the ingredients in *siljo*—a fermented puree made from *bakela duket* (fava bean flour), the milk of sunflower seeds, garlic, abesh (fenugreek), ginger, lemon juice and water.

Like most spices added to Ethiopian cooking, ground mustard seeds are used to enhance the flavor and aroma of the foods. And like most spices that are used in their cooking, the nutritional and health benefits of mustard seeds are not in the forefront of the cooks' thoughts. The spices and herbs are just part of the food blend. As you have already read, these herbs and spices also have many great health benefits.

Mustard seeds contain a good amount of vitamins, minerals, essential fatty acids and fiber, as well as phytonutrients. Of the vitamins, the predominating ones are the B-complex, those nutrients are important in energy production and nerve impulse transmission. These are: niacin, thiamine, riboflavin, folates, pyridoxine (Vitamin B6), and pantothenic acid. To a limited extent, mustard seeds also contain vitamins A, C, E, and K. Vitamin A and Vitamin E are fat-soluble antioxidants that help protect the body's cells and fat molecules against free radicals.

Of the minerals in mustard seeds, the most concentrated are calcium, copper, manganese, iron, selenium and zinc. As you may have read in the earlier chapters, these nutrients are essential for the proper functioning and protection of the body. Some of these minerals—manganese, zinc, copper, and selenium—are among the antioxidant enzymes (glutathione peroxidase, superoxide dismutase, and catalase) that help protect the body against cancer and cardiovascular diseases.

This wonderful condiment holds a good number of phytonutrients as well—sterols, curcuminoids, isothiocyanates, phenols, bioflavonoids, and carotenoids. All of these, as you may have read in this book or elsewhere, are important compounds in fighting cancer, in minimizing problems associated with heart diseases, and in slowing the aging of our bodies.

Sterols, found in all plants, are the equivalent of cholesterol. They don't harm your body but they help it. When ingested as part of the plant, sterols block cholesterol absorption in the intestine, thereby helping to lower blood cholesterol and lessen the health problems associated with this substance.

Curcuminoids are compounds that give plants their yellow color, like turmeric and some fruits and vegetables, for example. They, too, are important antioxidants. So are isothiocyanates, flavonoids, and carotenoids. Isothiocyanates are sulfur-containing molecules that occur naturally as glucosinolate compounds in all cruciferous vegetables such as broccoli, Brussels sprouts, cabbage, kale, turnips, collard greens and watercress. Research has shown that isothiocyanates can minimize the incidence of esophageal and lung cancers as well as others, including gastrointestinal cancer. A 2002 study published in the *International Journal for Vitamin and Nutrition Research* showed that isothiocyanates inhibited the replication of human cancer cells and accelerated their deaths. Similar compounds, also found in mustard seeds, were discovered to inhibit the growth of bladder cancer cells.

Mustard seeds contain a fair amount of essential amino acids as well as essential oils. The selenium level in mustard seeds is particularly high. This mineral, as was discussed earlier in the book, is good for heart health and in the prevention of cancer. Although, in western countries, mustard leaves and oils are also used in food preparation. In Ethiopia, it's mostly the seeds that are used. There are generally three types of mustard seeds: the black, white (in reality, it is a straw yellow), and brown. Brown is the most commonly used in Ethiopia.

Cited health benefits

In addition to their role in cancer prevention, mustard seeds are known to aid with the health of the cardiovascular system and as a treatment to respiratory disorders, such as chronic bronchitis, cold and sinus problems and asthma attacks. A poultice (bandage) made with mustard paste and applied to aching tissues and joints (as in rheumatism) can bring relief and comfort. A decoction made from mustard can help remove alcohol- and narcotic-related toxins from the body. Mustard seed oil has been found to increase lipid and glucose metabolism, which can be a benefit for diabetics.

People who suffer from psoriasis, acne, ringworms, contact dermatitis and other skin conditions can profit from the ingestion and application of mustard seeds. Mustard seeds are known to rejuvenate hair, enhance skin tone and invigorate the nerves.

In short, mustard seeds can contribute to your health, as well as enhance flavor and aroma in foods.

Caveat: Use mustard seeds in moderation. Anything in excess can be toxic. Consult your physician before you treat this spice like medicine.

Enjoy!

CHAPTER 16
Shinkoort (Red, Yellow, or White Onions)

Onions are the mainstays of nearly every Ethiopian dishes. They are one of the base ingredients in meats and legume foods. Sliced raw onions are also served with green salads and other vegetarian dishes. These layered, round objects make the food sweet, rich and tasty. In all these situations, onions are used to enhance flavor and give body or character to the foods. Most of us don't associate our consumption of onions to their value in our body. As you will see below, onions offer many great benefits to our health.

Onions contain a number of phytonutrients, many of which have been studied and found to help with several disease conditions. Let's look at the different areas that onions have been useful to us.

For starters, just like garlic, onions contain a great number of sulfur compounds and flavonoids called polyphenols. These compounds provide several benefits. Quercetin, anthocyanins and kaempferol are three well-studied flavonoids. They serve as antioxidants, antihistamine, anti-asthmatic and anti-inflammatory in our bodies. Incidentally, as with garlic, it's the sulfur compounds that give onions their characteristic smells and cause you to cry every time you chop them.

According to a 2012 study by the University of Colorado, quercetin can inhibit the growth of certain cancer cells. Another study published in the *International Journal of Nanomedicine* showed that kaempferol may inhibit the formation and growth of ovarian cancer. The sulfur compounds in onion are also known to kill bacteria, enhance circulation and lower the bad cholesterol level in the body.

These so called organo-sulfur compounds are also believed to minimize the risk from certain types of cancer. A November 2006 publication in the *"American Journal of Clinical Nutrition* found a positive correlation between the consumption of sulfur-rich foods and the lowering cancer incidence to the ovary, the colon and the esophagus. When onions are combined with turmeric, the synergy of the two substances can be great. Another 2006 study in *Clinical Gastroenterology and Hepatology* showed that when patients were given onion and turmeric together, they found that the two substances helped reduce the size and the number of pre-cancerous cells in the intestine. According to one doctor, regular consumption of onion can help detoxify the body. Ethiopians and those who cater to Ethiopian foods should find this revelation reassuring. Both turmeric (*ird*) and onion *(shinkoort*) are part of our daily diet.

High consumption of onions reportedly helps the body produce insulin, consequently lowering the blood sugar level. This theory was confirmed in a study published back in 1975 in the journal Clinica *Chemic Acta: The International Journal of Clinical Chemistry*. Additionally, onions are good for the heart. They can help lower blood pressure, inhibit the hardening of the arteries and keep the blood vessels supple and elastic, according Dr. Jonathan Stegall, an integrative medicine practitioner from John Creak, Georgia. Because of their antioxidant properties, onions also can help boost the immune system and protect the overall health of the body.

Yet, in another study, a regular consumption of onions was found to increase bone mass in post-menopausal women. The fibers in the onions should help with bowel movement, while their antioxidants help reduce the risk of gastric ulcer.

Onions also contain a number of vitamins and minerals. The highest concentration of the phytonutrients is found in the first layers of skins. Make sure you keep as many of the usable top layers as you can.

In closing, I couldn't help but think of the amount of onions used in Ethiopian foods, particularly with all of those meat dishes. After reading this chapter, you should be thinking beyond flavor and aroma, when you add or eat onion-based dishes. You should savor these foods. Think how much good they do for you every time you sit down to eat a meal with onions in them.

Caveats

For those sensitive individuals, onions may cause gas and bloating. For those with heartburn, consuming raw onions can worsen the condition. Consuming a large amount of green onions may interfere with a drug-thinning medicine, if you are on one.

CHAPTER 17
Tena Adam (Rue)

Tena Adam, or rue, is one more herb my mother grew in our garden. The strongly aromatic, pale green plant used to mystify and fascinate me. I think this was primarily because of its unusual, pungent smell, its clubbed leaves, and dainty, rounded yellow petals. Somehow, tena Adam seemed to me to have mystical and magical properties beyond its culinary uses. As you will see below, tena Adam has historically been associated with magic, mysticism, and witchcraft—my intuition was not imaginary.

Since ancient times, tena Adam has had many uses, both in food preparation and medicine, as well as in witchcraft. What I found fascinating as I read various articles in preparing to write this piece was that my childhood perception of tena Adam had historical antecedents.

During the European Middle Ages, people hung rue on their doors and windows as a protection against evil spirits. They rubbed their floors with it to kill fleas and to protect against plagues and pestilence. Christians sprinkled church entrances with the herb before performing mass and during exorcisms. Rue was considered sacred and the precious herb was planted around temples and churchyards. People carried bundles of rue twigs with them as they went about to ward off spells by witches. In courts and law offices, rue was strewn as a protection against diseases that might be carried by criminals. Even today there are people who believe that a rue plant in their garden can be protective of their home and bring harmony, prosperity and happiness.

Although rue is still used in many cultures as a flavoring agent, most people in the West are afraid to consume it. While the volatile oils extracted from rue are concentrated and can be poisonous if taken in large doses, some people believe that the rue leaves and berries are also poisonous.

Ethiopians have used rue berries in powdered berbere blend, in mitten shiro, and the leaves or berries in clarified butter for centuries. Rue berries are also often added to coffee and tea drinks. In all these situations, the dried and ground rue berries or leaves impart pungency and a pleasant aroma and flavor. The fresh leaves are sometimes added to boiling water or milk and given to children who have *kurtet* (pain) in their stomach and poor bowel movements. I have never heard or read stories about people who were poisoned by the use of tena Adam.

Like I mentioned, that concern should apply only to the concentrated volatile oil extract, which can be poisonous if taken in large doses. I suppose the same could happen if someone consumed too much of the berries or the leaves of tena Adam. For that matter, even water can be poisonous if consumed in excess.

Tena Adam's medical application

Medicinally, tena Adam is used as an antidote (corrective measure) against poisons, pestilences, and afflictions. The oil extract of tena Adam is used to counter the deadly effect of poisonous snakebites (like that of cobra and king cobra). The venom produced by these snakes' attacks is called neurotoxin because it affects the nervous system of the victim, causing them to suffocate and die. The venom released by vipers—such as copperheads, cottonmouths and most rattlesnakes—on the other hand, damages the blood vessels, causing the blood to become very thin and the victim eventually bleeds to death. This venom is called hemotoxic. Rue has no effect on hemotoxic venom.

To continue with rue's "anti-" effects, the herb is also known to be anti-arthritic, anti-rheumatic, anti-epileptic and anti-hysteric, to name but just a few. Rue's essential oils function as an anesthetic to all the affected bodily parts. These oils are also effective anti-bacterial and anti-fungal agents. Therefore these substances can help prevent infections both internally—like the colon, intestines and urinary tract, and externally—those that appear on the skin, such as ringworm, athlete's foot, and dermatitis. Furthermore, these oils have antiviral, anti-inflammatory, and antioxidant properties. In small amounts, these compounds can alleviate headaches.

The main active ingredient responsible for all these activities is called rutin, found as 7% to 8% in dried leaves. It's this compound that is the cause of the strong aroma and bitter taste when eaten in larger quantities. In small amounts, both the smell and taste are rather pleasant.

Tena Adam is also an excellent insect repellant; it discourages the presence of beetles and slugs and other vermin. Other uses include treatment in intestinal worms, mouth cancer, hepatitis, hemorrhage and fever. It's similarly used to treat arthritis, dislocations, swellings, sprains, tumors, warts, and aches associated with the ears, teeth and head.

In foods and beverages, rue and its oil are used as flavoring agents. In manufacturing, rue oil is used as fragrance in soaps and cosmetics.

Caveat: Ethiopians who read this reminder might find it surprising because, as mentioned, tena Adam is used in various dishes without having to worry about toxicity. Nonetheless, the literature warns that tena Adam (or rue), particularly the oil, can be poisonous when taken in excess. Pregnant women should never take tena Adam because it might cause uterine contractions, leading to abortion.

CHAPTER 18
Tikur Azmud (Black Cumin)

One of my favorite homemade loaves is one that is made with these black seeds in it. The English-speaking world calls it black cumin. Its technical name is *nigella sativa*. In Ethiopia, we endearingly call it tikur azmud. You will be astounded to know that these precious and wonderfully toothsome seeds have many health benefits besides their use to enhance the flavor of breads and other dishes.

Since olden times (more than 2000 years ago), black cumin seeds have been used to heal and improve the health of the body. Just to give you a perspective Hippocrates, the famed Greek medicine man, used black cumin to treat people with digestive disorders and other conditions. King Tutankhamen valued black cumin so much that it was one of the items found in his tomb. Supposedly, Cleopatra was a big fan of the herb not only for its remedial properties but also as a beauty aid. A continuous use of the black seed oil is found to improve the appearance of the skin, hair and nails. The Prophet Muhammad was more divinatory when he called black cumin "a remedy for every illness except death."

Modern researchers have discovered so many health benefits to black cumin that the founder of Islam's claim cannot be taken as mere exaggeration. In the last fifty-plus years, there have been over 200 different studies of the benefit of black cumin to the human body.

One study, conducted at the Cancer Research Laboratory of Hilton Head Island in South Carolina, showed that black cumin oil inhibited cancer growth by 50%, and stimulated immune cells and the production of interferon (protein molecules that protect the cells from the damaging effects of viruses). Additionally, black cumin oil increased the production of bone marrow cells by as much as 250%.

The bone marrow cells consist of the red cells, white cells and platelets. As you may know, white cells are one of our immune forces that fight viruses, bacteria and fungi. The red cells carry oxygen, the element that helps burn the food we eat into energy. Platelets are cells that help our blood to clot.

Black cumin oil was also found to be beneficial in treating cardiovascular diseases, diabetes, kidney disease, and asthma, as well as cancer of the pancreas, lungs, kidneys, liver, prostate, skin, and breast. The list goes on.

Black cumin oil is known to help fight colds and flu, stress, tired legs and muscles, arthritis, rheumatism, bruises, high blood pressure, diarrhea, hair loss, all types of aches (headache, backache, earache, etc.), stomach and intestinal problems, skin fungus, acne, allergies, sinus problems, and even in subduing a baby that cries uncontrollably.

Regarding the use of black cumin seeds to treat aches and pains, I recently had a tooth pulled out. I chewed a pinch of the herb on the good side of my mouth every so often and the relief I got was almost magical. What else?

In several animal models, this remarkable herb was found to be a potent agent against inflammations of the brain and spinal cord (encephalomyelitis), the swelling of soft tissues from excessive accumulation of fluid (edema), inflammation of the colon (colitis), inflammation of the silk-like membrane of the abdominal wall and that covers the organs (peritonitis), and arthritis. Black cumin seed oil can also be used to treat hemorrhoids, hepatitis, fever, cough and tapeworm, as well as nasal dryness.

Furthermore, you can use black cumin oil to enhance your physical appearance. This can be achieved by consuming the oil, a teaspoon of it with your warm tea or soup, or by adding the same amount into your personal cream and applying it on your face and hands. It's known to help with skin blemishes and conditions like eczema, psoriasis, acne, lines and wrinkles. For lasting effect, though, it's better if you consume the seeds or oil for a protracted time. Then, according to the reports, you are supposed to have lustrous hair, nails and skin.

What makes black cumin seeds and oil such versatile curative agents?

The most studied active ingredient in black cumin seed is called thymoquinone. It's this compound, which acts as an antioxidant, fighting and killing cancer cells and bacteria and fungus that cause inflammations in the body. There are many other compounds in black cumin seeds, including vitamins, minerals, and fatty acids, which together have a powerful effect on the health and wellness of the body.

Other researchers who studied tikur azmud's oil suggest that one should take a teaspoon of the oil, alone or with warm tea, an hour before a meal once or twice a day.

If you have access to tikur azmud oil capsules, which are sold in Indian or Middle Eastern as well as some Ethiopian food stores (see caveat below), use this version of the spice. However, consuming ground tikur azmud with your favorite food in similar amounts can also have positive results. Alternatively, you can soak the seeds overnight, then warm over a stove, filter, and drink as tea.

If you purchase black cumin oil, heed this warning. According to Tony Isaacs, natural health researcher and author of *Cancer's Natural Enemy*, there are many different products sold under the umbrella of black (black cumin seed oil, black onion seed, black caraway seed, and black sesame seed), but the true product is the one labeled as *nigella sativa*.

All these accounts are not just products of folklore or old wives' tales. As you will see from the list of references at the end of the book, most of what we have discussed here are results of scientific studies that have been conducted in various institutions around the world.

Black cumin seeds and oil indeed appear to be a cure for nearly everything and anything under the sun except death.

How to used tikur azmud

Most of you know the various recipes for loaves and as blends with other spices. For those who don't, when you make dough for loaf or other breads, put in a dash of the black seeds and mix thoroughly. A pinch or two will be sufficient, depending on the amount of batter you have.

For teas: Boil hot water, throw in a teaspoon of tikur azmud, steep for 15-20 minutes, filter and drink. You can also add honey, lemon and black pepper to enhance the flavor.

Add ground black cumin to stir-fry dishes, salads and casseroles to give these foods a new twist in flavor and taste. Include lemon and cilantro for maximum effect.

Caveats

1. Pregnant woman should not take black cumin oil or the seeds in large quantities. They should consult their doctor before using it.

2. Black cum seeds have blood pressure lowering effect and therefore not recommended to those who suffer from low blood pressure.

3. Black cumin oil should not be taken plain and with a full stomach. It should be mixed in water, tea, juice or honey and taken and 1-2 hours before a meal.

4. Never mix the intake of black cumin with prescription or other drugs.

If taking the seeds, they must be heated. Never take the seeds that have not been heated as they will upset the stomach.

CHAPTER 19
Timiz (Long Pepper)

Timiz (botanically known as *Piper Carpense*) is generally found as part of the spice blends like mekelesha and berbere. It has a pungent smell with properties of both coriander and black pepper, but hotter and sweeter. Timiz is used to enrich the flavor of meat dishes and sometimes coffee and tea.

Timiz is produced by a climbing vine shrub with heart-shape, luxuriant leaves and white flowers that resemble a bottle-cleaning brush on a stick. Upon maturity, tiny poppy-seed size berries are embedded like cornrows on an ear but in a winding pattern, giving rise to its Amharic name, *timiz* or twisted. These berries or fruits are yellowish-orange but the individual spikes (the whole ear of corn structure) are red when ripe but turn black upon drying.

In Ethiopia, timiz grows in the Bonga coffee forest of the South-west section of the country. Despite its high demand, its production is reportedly low. There is also an imported timiz, which is referred to as *yeferenge*—a white person's— timiz, to distinguish it from the homegrown, *yehabehsa* (a generic name for Ethiopians) variety. Yeferenge timiz actually comes from India and in the general literature it bears its name of origin or it's known is simply as "long pepper". This variety has a stronger aroma and more spicy than the Ethiopian version. The Indian timiz (which incidentally also grows in Malaysia, Indonesia, Singapore, Sri Lanka, Nepal, and South-East Asia) is a lot more expensive, both because of the tariff levied on it and because of its supposed superior quality.

Interestingly, timiz is not popular elsewhere in the world other than the countries where it's grown. It's an old spice. During the Roman Empire, it was the preferred food flavoring-agent. When the black pepper was introduced, timiz fell out of favor.

Besides its culinary uses, timiz has many health benefits. In Ethiopia, it's used to alleviate *kurtmat*—the stinging aches in the bones and muscles, *wugat*—sharp pains in chest and abdomen or *kurtet*—the cutting sensations in the intestines and stomach. In other countries, long pepper has traditionally been used to relieve congestion in the chest and respiratory tract (such as asthma, bronchitis and coughs). It's also used to facilitate digestion and improve bowel movement.

Long pepper oils have antiseptic properties and can help heal wounds and cuts, suppress pain and reduce inflammation. Have involuntary muscle spasms like hiccups? Drink a tea of timiz or mix the powder of it with honey and swallow it. It can help stop it. Since timiz stimulates the reproductive system, it's often used as an aphrodisiac. Long pepper has similarly been used as a calming or sedative agent to those who suffer from insomnia and epilepsy.

Moreover, This interesting spice has been used to treat a host of other conditions: headaches, toothaches, intestinal worms and snakebites. In addition, long pepper has been used to treat Vitamin B1 deficiency, stroke and as a remedy to ministerial cramps, infertility and as an aid during and after childbirth.

Many of us, who live in cities and towns where modern medicine is readily available, probably won't reach for the timiz bottle in our kitchen cabinets to treat or cure many of the maladies listed above, but the point is as we have already seen, all the herbs and spices we use to enhance flavor and taste house many wonderful benefits to our health. They may help you live a healthy, long life.

Enjoy!

CHAPTER 20
Tosign (Savory)

In Ethiopian cooking, tosign, can appear both in the berbere and mitten shiro blends. It's also added to boiling water and drank as tea. Besides its overall tonic effect on the body, tosign tea reportedly can also help lower an abnormally high blood pressure.

In western societies and a number of other cultures, tosign (or savory) has been used as a spice and, more commonly, as an herb. Savory is employed to stimulate appetite and improve digestion, as palliative for sore throat, and as carminative to bloating and gas. It's also used to treat headaches and lessen the problems associated with coughing.

Tea made of savory can be effective against the flu, particularly when taken together with chamomile, colt's foot and honey. A combination of savory and black currant tea is supposed to alleviate or even cure severe and spasmodic cough.

The leaves of savory are rich in vitamins, minerals, fiber and phytonutrients. Many of these phytochemicals are antioxidants that can help boost the immune system, reduce bad cholesterol levels, and protect the heart and blood vessels.

The aroma, color and flavor found in herbs and spices are often a result of the complex organic compounds contained in them. The aromas they emit come from volatile essential oils.

Savory, like most herbs, has a number of these smelly substances and they include thymol, carvacrol, aslinalool, camphene and a few others. The first two compounds are the most studied. Thymol has been shown to have antiseptic and antifungal properties. Carvacrol has been shown to control the growth of several bacteria, including E. coli and Bacillus cereus. Carvacrol reportedly imparts a pleasant, tangy taste. Because of these attributes and its anti-microbial properties, carvacrol has been used in food preparation and preservation.

Savory is a storehouse of vitamins, minerals and fibers. In 100 hundred grams of dry savory, you can expect to find 474% of the DV for iron, 265% of DV for manganese, 210% of DV for calcium, and 94% of DV for magnesium. And you can get 120% of DV for dietary fiber. Its content of potassium, zinc selenium, and vitamins A, B6 and C are reported to be high as well.

Savory can be used to treat problems affecting the urinary tract and when you have sore throat, diarrhea, indigestion or diabetes to relieve the problems associated with frequent thirst. The juice of savory can be applied directly on the skin to treat insect bites. This herb can function as a tonic to enhance the overall health of the body. In some cultures, savory is even used as an aphrodisiac.

For many of savory's benefits, you can add it to your favorite dishes, or make it into a tea and drink it periodically. You want to add honey or sugar to taste, to sweeten the infusion. The Addition of black currant to savory tea can stop a severe bout of coughing.

Gamma aminoburyic acid (GABA) is a natural chemical and neurotransmitter that calms and normalizes your brain and the nervous system. Its primary function is as an inhibitor, preventing over overstimulation. It does this by counteracting glutamate—the brain's major excitatory neurotransmitter. When GABA binds to a receptor, it prevents stimulation by glutamate. When GABA levels are inadequate, overstimulation due to high levels of glutamate can occur. A low level of GABA can lead to anxiety, insomnia, depression, moodiness and a number of other disorders. There are many ways you can correct these problems nutritionally, as well as with medication. Reportedly, savory can have a positive impact on your GABA level.

As mentioned above, you can add savory to your favorite foods or make into a tea and consume regularly when you have conditions that the herb is known to treat. You can also use this herb as part of your everyday diet to take advantage of its tonic properties.

Enjoy!

PART III
Selected Ethiopian Food Recipes

The Super Spice Blends Found in Most Ethiopian Cooking

These spice mixes are used in hot meat dishes as well as serve as flavor enhancers in other foods.

1. Berbere (the classic blend)

Berbere is the foundation of all the red meat and vegetable stews as well as the raw material for *awaze*—a paste—in Ethiopian cuisine. Berbere is a blend of many spices, many of which have been already described in this book. Berbere is a nutritionally dense food—rich in vitamins, minerals, phytonutrients and fiber. Traditionally, making berbere is a long and involved process—taking several days and often the help of family members or neighbors, particularly with removing the wood part of the dried jalapeno peppers. It's made in large batches to last six months to a year.

Customarily, there are no measuring cups or scales. A woman's eyes, hand, fingers or imagination serve as measuring devices. A large canvas or skin mat is necessary to dry some of the ingredients individually. A woman would often gather the jalapeno pepper and try to guess how many hand-cups or pinches of the small ingredients it would take to create the proper blend of the berbere blend.

Berbere preparation for a family of four will last one year

1. Snip the stalks of the jalapeno with one's fingers

2. Wash the final trimmed peppers and spread on canvas to dry in the sun

3. Mill the dried jalapeno and keep aside.

    a. Measure one or two handfuls of tena adam (rue) berries and place in a wooden mortar.

    b. De-shell 30-40 garlic cloves and add to the mortar.

    c. Measure a handful of beso bela and add to the mortar.

    d. Peel and mince ginger and measure in a cupped hand and add to the mortar.

    e. Pound the above items together into a paste.

4. Combine the paste with milled pepper (step 3) and mix thoroughly in a large bowl.

5. Cover tightly and leave it aside for two days, for the aroma and flavor of each ingredient to infuse into each other.

6. On the third day open the bowl, transfer the blend on to a matt and let it dry for a day or two in the sun.

7. In a heated skillet toast lightly the dried mixture to bring out the flavors and make sure that it has dried completely.

8. Cool down and mill the mixture.

9. In a separate batch, measure out coriander seeds, fenugreek seeds, black peppercorns, allspice, cardamom pods, and cloves and toast in a pan, mixing continuously with a wooden spoon for about 4 minutes. Take away from fire and let cool.

10. In a separate container mix beso bela, netch azmud, tikur azmud and tosign and grind.

11. Combine the blends from #8, #9 and #10 and mix thoroughly.

The final product should be fire red, wonderfully aromatic and flavorful, ready to be used as the base spice blend for chicken, meat and legume dishes as well as for a number of other foods. Because in the traditional way of making berbere measuring devices are not used, the flavor, aroma and color can be as individual as the person making it.

Below is the modern, standardized berbere recipe.

Ingredients

2 tsp. coriander seeds

1 tsp. fenugreek seeds

1⁄2 tsp. black peppercorns

1⁄4 tsp. whole allspice

6 white cardamom pods

4 whole cloves

1⁄2 cup dried onion flakes

12 garlic cloves

5 dried chilies de árbol, stemmed, seeded,

and broken into small pieces

3 tbsp. paprika powder (to deepen the color)

1⁄2 tsp. ground nutmeg

1⁄2 tsp. ground ginger

1⁄2 tsp. ground cinnamon

Directions:

1. In a small skillet, combine coriander seeds, fenugreek seeds, black pepper-corns, allspice, cardamom pods, and cloves. Toast spices over medium heat, swirling skillet constantly until fragrant for about 4 minutes.

2. Let cool slightly.

3. Transfer to a spice grinder along with onion flakes and mill until they turn into fine powder. Add chilies, and mill with the other spices until fine.

4. Transfer the mixture to a bowl and stir in the paprika powder, salt, nutmeg, ginger, and cinnamon. Store in an airtight container and use as needed.

5. Store in an airtight container and use as needed.

2. Mekelesha –The finishing spice for wots

Ingredients

1/2 tsp. coriander seeds

5 cloves of garlic

1/2 tsp. cumin

1/4 tsp. nutmeg, freshly ground

1/2 tsp. cinnamon powder

1 tsp. black pepper

1/2 tsp. Indian long pepper

Mill these together to produce a wonderful aroma and a gray, nutmeg-like blend. Store in a tightly covered container and use as needed.

3. Mitmita

Mitmita is a classic hot spice blend used with kitfo and raw beef cubes. It's also frequently served as condiment with main course dishes. It can be eaten with plain injera or sprinkled over bean dishes before serving.

In Ethiopia, the bird's eye chili is usually collected from the garden, and sun-dried and combined with the ingredients below and milled.

Ingredients

2 lbs. bird's eye chilies

1/2 tsp. black mustard seeds

2 tbsp. whole cloves

1/4 cup kewrerima (Ethiopian cardamom) seeds

3/4 cup sea salt

2 tbsp. ground cinnamon (optional)

1 tbsp. cumin seeds (optional)

1 tbsp. ground ginger (optional)

Directions:

1. Combine the seed and whole chilies and dry roast, making sure some of the seeds don't pop and fly away.

2. Remove from fire and let cool

3. Combined the powered options with the chilies and seeds

4. Grind to a fine powder in a coffee grinder or mortar and pestle

5. Store in an airtight container

The resulting powder is light or dark orange, depending upon which ingredients you have included.

4. Mitten Shiro

Making mitten shiro is as tedious and involved as creating the berbere blend. Like berbere, once you make it, it will last you for six months or more. As we mentioned before, there is no standardized recipe, as each household creates its own. Although most of the ingredients listed below are used across the board, there are also creative women who take away one or two ingredients and add their own. Since traditionally there have not been measuring devices for the ingredients, the quantity and therefore the taste of the mitten shiro may vary from one formulation to another. The following recipe is created in approximation to what most women use to make the mitten shiro blend.

There are generally four types of legumes consumed in Ethiopia. These are peas, lentils, wide beans, also known as fava beans, and chickpeas. When we talk about shiro wot, we usually mean the sauce made from peas flour. However, for mitten shiro all four legumes can be used, in part, because peas, as the most consumed, can be expensive.

Ingredients

8 cups peas

3 cups fava beans

4 cups chickpeas

4 cups lentils

3 cups berbere

1 cup tena adam (rue) seeds

1 koseret (oregano, a substitute)

3 heads of garlic, peeled and finely chopped

1 cup red onion

2 tbsp. fenugreek

1 cup ginger, finely chopped

1 cup beso bela (sacred basil)

12 kewrerima pods (just the seeds)

2 tbsp. coriander powder

1 tbsp. bishop's weed (netch azmud)

2 tbsp. cloves

2 tbsp. cinnamon

Salt as needed

2.5 cups water

Making the mitten shiro

1. Wash peas, chickpeas, beans and lentils individually and boil each in water. You need to do them this way because these legumes cook at different rates.

2. On a large canvas spread each item in its own lot and let dry in the sun or in the oven at low heat. Grind to powder at home or send out to be milled.

3. De-shell the cardamom pods and grind the seeds.

4. Combine the onion, garlic, ginger and koseret and smash in mortar and pestle into a paste. Spread on mat and let dry in the sun. Once the mixture/ blend is completely dry, grind at home or send out to be milled.

5. In a heavy skillet, roast in low heat the fenugreek, cloves, coriander, sacred basil, cinnamon bark, bishop's weed for 3 minutes. Take off heat, cool and grind these as well.

6. In large bowl, mix the berbere, the shiro powder and the spice blends (3-5 above). This is your mitten shiro. Transfer to a container with tight lid and store in a dry place.

Mitten shiro's 20-30% of total weight reportedly is spices and salt.

There is also Netch shiro. It's used to make alicha shiro wot. With Netch shiro, the pea flour is combined with ground garlic, ginger, mekelesha and salt. Fifteen to twenty percent the weight of netch shiro is purportedly spices and salt.

You can see, just as with berbere, these seemingly simple food ingredients, are packed with many good things that are healthy for you. This is so particularly in light of all the spices and their associated benefits we discussed in the previous chapters.

No pure sugars, excessive amounts of fat and salt and there are no extraneous fillers, artificial colors or preservatives in these foods. Both the colors and preservatives are part of the natural spices and herbs.

5. Niter Kibbeh (Clarified Butter)

Clarified, spiced butter is one of the major components of the Ethiopian cooking. It enhances the flavor, taste and aroma of foods. Traditionally, it's used in cooked meats, vegetables, as well as legume dishes. During the fast days, women use only oils to prepare non-dairy and meat foods. As you can see from the Measurements and Ingredients, it is beautifully aromatic and tasty and you can't eat enough of it once you start. It can go with anything.

Makes 1-1/2 cups

Ingredients

1 pound unsalted butter

1/2 medium red onion, chopped

1 garlic clove, minced

1 tbsp. minced ginger

1 tsp. fenugreek seeds

1 tsp. ground cumin

1 tsp. kewrerima or green cardamom seeds

1 tsp. dried beso bela (or oregano)

1/2 tsp. ground turmeric

7 sweet basil leaves

Directions:

1. Melt the butter in a saucepan over low heat, stirring frequently. As it cooks, it begins to froth, bubbles building on top. Skim and discard the foam, do so continuously until you see no more of the bubbles. Make sure to stir occasionally so it won't turn brown on you.

2. Add the onion, ginger, fenugreek, cumin, garlic, cardamom, oregano, turmeric, and basil and let it simmer for 15 minutes but still stir occasionally.

3. Remove from the heat and let it cool.

4. Strain into a container using a finely meshed sieve.

5. Cover the lid and store in the fridge.

Clarified butter's unique features:

1. It has a longer shelf-life than regular butter.

2. It has a high smoke point. This means you can cook foods with it at higher temperatures than you would with regular butter. It's ideal for stir-fried dishes. This is because clarifying the butter removes a lot of the milk solids and other salts, which cause the regular butter to burn.

Food Recipes

Injera (Ethiopian Flat, Leaven Bread)

So you think you can make injera, eh?

As you have read in the previous chapters, why Ethiopian food is textured, tasty and healthy is due to the spices, the whole-grain foods and preparation techniques. Making many of the dishes given below is very easy once you have berbere, Mekelesha, the necessary spices to make niter kebbeh and other special-ized dishes. Producing authentic injera from pure teff, however, will take a keen understanding of the temperature and time needed to ferment the dough or batter, your patience and willingness to try and try again if you didn't succeed the first time. Although it's relatively simple to make teff injera in Ethiopia, people in the United States find it difficult to do so. For this reason they often had to add barley, whole wheat or self-rising flour.

Anybody can make flat bread out of the teff dough, but to be called injera, it has to meet certain expected standards.

1. The top of the injera has to stare at you with its thousand eyes, steady and unblinking. And there should never be closed ones anywhere on the surface—more or less.

2. This injera has to feel spongy, stretchy, and delicate to the touch.

3. Since it's generally made from fermented batter, it characteristically must taste sour and tart.

From this list, the first two are often the hardest to achieve on the first try, particularly to those who don't know about the nuances of preparing and fermenting the teff dough and making the injera from it. This is so because there are some processes and conditions to be met in order to make a credible injera. How well have you kneaded and prepared the dough? What is the ambient temperature where you keep the fermenting dough? What is the quality of the flour? Is the *mitad* (grill) clay or metal? Is mitad sufficiently heated before you pour the dough on it? And is the dough runny enough when you pour it onto the mitad?

Once you understand these requirements, you're ready to try the recipe below.

The perfect injera

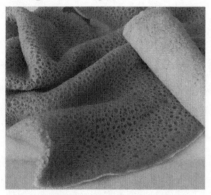

Spongy, stretchy and delicate like a fine fabric

An advice and wisdom

Regardless of how the injera comes out—flat and soulless as a tortilla or bold and wide-eyed like someone high in caffeine—what ultimately matters is the nutritional value of the injera. And as you saw earlier, teff has a lot of good things for your health. If it's for your own consumption, the aesthetic details of the injera are probably not that important. If you have dinner guests, one of whom is the Royal Highness of Ethiopia, then I'd keep it locked in my *madd-bet*—kitchen house. On a serious note, let's talk about our teff injera recipe.

Cooking items:

A large metal or plastic bowl

Flat-end wooden spoon (optional)

A measuring cup

A 10- to 12-inch skillet with a glass cover (ideally)

A large plate or tray

Yeast powder

A dish towel

A small clean cloth or paper napkin

1 tbsp. of vegetable oil

The recipe:

3.5 cups brown teff flour

1 cup whole wheat flour

1/2 cup all-purpose flour

4 cups filtered or distilled water

1 tbsp. yeast powder

Preparation:

1. Combine the three flours in the bowl

2. Add the water and mix the content with the spatula or your washed hand.

3. Keep adding the water until the mixture is thick and moist enough for kneading. Beat it with the spatula or your hand for a minute or so.

4. Heat 1 cup of water till hot. Remove from stove and add the yeast and Mix it thoroughly.

5. Set aside for 15-20 minutes to activate the yeast. Adding half a teaspoon of brown sugar can help speed up the activation.

6. Add the yeast-water mixture to the dough and blend thoroughly. Cover it with the dish towel (or a plate) and leave it overnight or until evening time if you made it in the morning. If you place the dough near a warm stove, it can rise quicker. If you use natural yeast, generated from a previous batch of dough, fermenting the new batter generally takes 3-5 days.

Baking:

1. Heat the skillet at the medium setting of your cook top plate dial.

2. Mix the dough with spoon or a washed hand.

3. Add 1/2 a cup of water (if it needs it) so the dough becomes runny.

4. Apply the vegetable oil onto the cloth or napkin and rub the skillet bottom and sides with it, so the baking injera won't stick to the bottom.

5. Pour half a cup of the dough onto the center of the skillet. After quickly putting down the cup, grab the skillet by the handle, lift and swirl it, until the dough spreads and covers the bottom evenly. Put it back down on the hot plate or grill. If the skillet is sufficiently heated, the dough hisses as it touches the pan and you swirl it around. This is a good indication, assuming you have met all the other requirements the injera is probably going to come out alright.

6. Cover immediately and wait for 2.5 to 3 minutes. If the cover is clear you can watch as the white dough turns brown progressively, until it eventually fades completely.

7. Remove the lid and check to see if the edges have begun to lift. If they have, pry one end with the spatula, insert it all the way and lift and transfer the freshly-baked injera on to the plate. Now you made your first perfect injera, the rest is history. Keep baking until all the dough is used up.

Sometimes the edges of the baking injera may not lift. In this case, pick them with a spatula until you have access to the whole bread to lift it.

There are many other recipes for making injera. In the United States, the Ethiopian restaurants that make those beautiful and delicate injeras, use higher amounts of wheat or barley flours—60% to70%—than I've included in the recipe above. Nothing is wrong with these injeras. It's just you're not getting the benefits of teff as much as you would when preparing the injera or loaf from the brown grain. Whole barley and whole wheat flours have their own beneficial nutrients as well.

Making a loaf out of teff flour

Use the same recipe but make the batter thicker like regular injera dough. You can add half a cup of brown sugar and a tea spoon of anise seeds. You can let it ferment for a few hours or can make it right away. If you bake it shortly after you make the dough, the loaf will be heavy and hardens when it cools down. If you baked yeast-risen dough it will be lighter and spongy. You can also make kita out of the freshly made dough. This bread is thin like a pizza crust. If you're sweet-toothed, you can sprinkle it with honey or a little bit of brown sugar and serve. You don't need the sweetener; the plain kita is just as tasty.

Another remarkable thing about teff is, it's filling. You can have just a loaf made from teff flour and tea or coffee and go about your task in the morning without feeling hungry. And you will have so much energy, too. If you're trying to lose or manage weight, replacing your regular breads with teff injera, kita or loaf can be the best alternative to achieving your goal or desire.

Meat Dishes

Doro Wot (Red Chicken Stew)

One of the most popular Ethiopian dishes

Ingredients

3 finely chopped red onions (preferably)

1/3 cup berbere

4 cloves of garlic

1 tsp. of finely chopped ginger root

1/4 tsp. ground cardamom

1/8 tsp. ground nutmeg

1/4 tsp. ground fenugreek

1 tsp. freshly ground black pepper[1]

1 tsp. table salt

1/4 cup niter kibbeh or ½ cup extra virgin olive oil

1-3 cups filtered or distilled water

4-6 hard-boiled eggs

6-8 pieces of chicken (legs, drumstick or thighs and wings), thoroughly washed, squeezed and dab-dried

(Serves 6-8 people)

Trivia: In Ethiopia getting the chicken ready for cooking is as elaborate and as making the stew itself. Every trace of fat or tissue that is not meat has to be removed. Then the chicken pieces are washed several times.

---

1   If you have mekelesha, use it instead.

Making the doro wot

1. In a large pot (preferably clay or enamel) sauté the onions in medium heat, till they turn brown. This can take 3- 4 minutes.

2. Add 1/2 a cup of water to dissolve the onion its constituents and simmer for 3-4 minutes for 3-4 minutes.

3. Add the berbere and let it simmer for 5 minutes.

4. Add the niter kebbeh or the oil and let it cook for 3 minutes.

5. Add the garlic and the rest of the spices (except black pepper) and let it cook for 3-4 minutes.

6. Add the rest of the water and let the contents cook for 5 minutes more.

7. Add the chicken pieces and make sure they are beneath the surface of the simmering sauce. If not, add enough water to cover them.

8. Lower the heat and let it cook for 15-20 minutes.

9. De-shell the eggs and poke them with a fork or straw, creating as many holes as you can.

10. Check to see if the chicken pieces are well cooked. They must feel tender.

11. Now add the eggs, and stir the content well so the eggs get coated with the sauce.

12. Cover and simmer for 4 to 6 minutes more.

13. Finally, add the salt and black pepper or mekelesha and stir.

14. Remove from heat and let it cool.

You're now ready to reward yourself: feast over one of Ethiopia's classic meat dishes known as doro wot! Ideally, you would want to eat your doro wot with injera. If you don't have one, you can still enjoy it over rice or with regular bread, together with salad and other vegetables on the side.

Enjoy!

Sega Wot

Ingredients

2-3 lbs. lean, cubed beef

3 red onions, finely minced

3 cloves of garlic, finely minced

2 tsp. minced or powdered ginger

1/2 cup berbere

1/4 cup niter kibbeh or extra virgin olive oil

1 tsp. cardamom seeds or powder

1 tsp. black pepper (or mekelesha)

Making the sega wot:

1. Add the onion to a large pot with a lid and let it simmer for 15 minutes. Don't over stir.

2. Add 1 tbsp. of the niter kebbeh or oil and cook for 5 minutes or so, until the onion turns dark brown, but not burnt dark.

3. Add the berbere, 1/4 cup of hot water and the rest of the niter kebbeh or oil and let the mixture simmer at low heat for 15 minutes or so. Add the beef (a piece at a time), the garlic and 1/4 cup of hot water, put back the cover and let it cook for 12 minutes. Stir occasionally.

4. Add the garlic, reduce heat and let everything cook for 7-10 minutes, until the meat is tender.

5. Add salt (to taste), cardamom and black pepper (or mekelesha) and continue to simmer for another 5 minutes, still at low heat.

Remove from fire, cool to a comfortable temperature and sever over injera or rice. This wot can serve 6-8 people.

Doro Alicha (chicken stewed in turmeric sauce)

Ingredients

- 4 yellow onions, finely chopped
- 1/4 cup olive oil or
- 1/4 cup niter kibbeh
- 3 tbsp. of finely minced garlic
- 1 tbsp. finely chopped ginger root
- 1/2 cup dry white wine or honey wine
- 3 cups of water
- 4 hard-boiled eggs
- 6 drumsticks and 6 thigh bone-in chicken meat
- 1/4 tsp. turmeric (for light amber color)
- 1 freshly ground black pepper
- 1 tsp. ground cardamom

Preparing the doro alicha

1. In a heavy enamel or iron stewpot, cook the onions over moderate heat for about 5 minutes or until translucent by adding water as needed.

2. Add the garlic and ginger and continue to sauté for 5 more minutes, adding water as needed.

3. Add the niter kibbeh and stir for another 5 minutes, till everything is well blended.

4. Add the dry white wine, bring to a boil.

5. Cook briskly, uncovered, for about 5 minutes, stirring occasionally.

6. Gently drop the chicken into the simmering sauce. Stir carefully until the chicken is well coated with the sauce. Add water if needed.

7. Reduce heat, cover, and simmer for 10 minutes.

8. Remove from heat, let it cool down and serve with injera or over rice.

Courtesy: Brundo Ethiopian spices

Kitfo (Steak Tartar)

Ingredients

3 pounds freshly ground, very lean beef

1 tsp. mitmita

1 tsp. kowrerima

1 tsp. salt (as needed)

1/4 cup of niter kibbeh

Preparing the kitfo

Mix ground beef and the rest of the ingredients thoroughly. Heat pan and sear lightly and serve with Injera.

Vegetarian Dishes

There are many vegetarian dishes in Ethiopian cooking. The most common ones are shiro wot (prepared from pea or a combination of 3 or 4 legume flours), kik wot (made from split peas), miser wot (from split or whole lentils), mixed vegetables and Ethiopian salad (see below). You find these in nearly all Ethiopian restaurants. The most complex dishes are generally made at home for special occasions like a wedding, during the fast days or big annual festivals.

Here are a few vegetarian recipes.

Shiro Wot

Ingredients

1.5 cup shiro (ground pea or chickpea flour)

(Normally purchased from an Ethiopian store. You can also make your own following the recipes given on Page 73.)

1 large onion, finely chopped

1/2 cup olive oil or niter kebbeh (if you have one)

4 cloves of garlic

1 tbsp. berbere

1 tsp. salt (to taste)

3 cups of water

Making the shiro wot:

1. Sauté the onion in the oil in a medium-size pot for 3 minutes.

2. Add the berbere, a little bit of water, cover top and let the contents simmer.

3. In a bowl, dissolve the shiro in the remaining water completely by adding the flour gradually. Transfer the resulting mixture into the cooking pot. Alternatively, you can add the shiro directly but slowly to the pot as you continue to stir the content. Just make sure it doesn't become lumpy.

4. Add the salt to taste and cook for 25-30 minutes at low heat. The shiro wot can be served runny or thick. If the latter, add more shiro powder (or a thickener like corn starch) and let it cook longer.

5. If you have niter kebbeh, add a table spoon of it to further enhance the flavor.

6. Serve on injera or with rice.

Misir Wot (Lintel Stew)

Ingredients

4 cups of lintel

1 large onion finely minced

2 tbsp. niter kebbeh or 1/2 cup extra virgin oil

5 cloves of garlic finely minced

2 tbsp. Berbere

2 tbsp. salt (as needed)

8-10 cups of water

Making the misir wot:

1. In a large pot simmer onion, garlic, and berbere with the butter or oil for 8-10 minutes.

2. Add the lintels and water and continue to simmer at low heat for about 25 minutes. Stir occasionally and check to see if the lintels are completely cooked. If done, turn off heat source.

3. Serve with injera or over rice.

Kik Wot (split yellow peas stew)

Ingredients

3 cups of split yellow peas

2 large onions fine minced

2 tbsp. niter kebbeh or ½ cup of extra virgin olive oil

4 cloves of garlic

2 tsp. turmeric

2 tsp. salt (as needed)

8-10 cups of water

Making the kik wot

1. Add onions, garlic, turmeric and the butter or oil and simmer for 8-10 minutes.

2. Add the split peas and water and continue to simmer at low heat for 20-30 minutes.

3. Stir often to make sure the contents don't stick to the bottom of pot.

4. Once the peas are completely cooked, remove pot and serve hot.

Mixed Vegetables

Ingredients

1 large onion, minced

1/4 of cabbage head

3 cloves garlic, minced

1 tsp ginger, minced

2 medium potatoes, chopped

2 medium carrots, chopped

2 tbsp. extra virgin olive oil

1 tsp. salt (to taste)

1 tbsp. turmeric

Making the mixed vegetables

1. Sauté onion, garlic, ginger and chilies in oil for 10 minutes.
2. Add potatoes, carrots and cabbage and cook for 25 minutes
3. Add salt and turmeric and simmer for 5 minutes
4. Once done remove from heat. Serve with injera or over rice.

Gomen (Collard Green)

Ingredients

2 bunches collard greens, finely chopped

2 red, yellow or white onions, minced

1 tbsp. niter kebbeh or 1/4 extra virgin olive oil

3 medium size tomatoes minced

3 cloves of garlic minced

2 jalapenos, chopped (optional)

2 cups of filtered or distilled water

Making the gomen

1. Wash the collard green thoroughly and run through a spinner or dab-dry with towel.

2. Snip and discard the stalks.

3. Chop the leaves finely.

4. Heat a deep skillet, sauté onions and tomatoes in the niter kebbeh or oil for 4-6 minutes.

5. Add the minced garlic and cook for 4 minutes, cover pot and cook at medium heat.

6. Add the sliced jalapenos and salt as needed.

Serve hot with injera or use as a side dish to a main course.

The Ethiopian Green Salad

Ingredients

1/2 a head of green lettuce

1 thinly sliced tomato

2 garlic cloves, finely minced

1 tbsp. each: extra-virgin olive oil and white wine vinegar (mixed and shaken together)

1 medium onion (red, yellow or white), chopped in short thin trips

3 tbsp. parsley, chopped

3 tbsp. freshly squeezed lemon juice

1 tsp. black pepper, freshly ground

1/4 tsp. ginger, finely minced

1/2 red bell pepper

Salt to taste

Making the Ethiopian green salad

1. In large salad bowl, mix vinegar, garlic, oil, ginger and black pepper and whisk gently

2. Add lettuce, onion slices, tomatoes, bell pepper and parsley.

3. Add lemon and toss well. Serve as a regular side dish.

All five vegetarian dishes are served over injera.

Misir wot, kik wot, gomen, mixed vegetables and the Ethiopian salad.

Azifa

Lentils never grew in the highlands of Ethiopia where I come from. So I don't ever remember eating them when I grew up. They are lowland, warm climate legumes. In the towns and cities I lived, I had a variety of dishes made from lentils. One of them was azifa.

Ingredients

2 cups green lentils

3 cloves of fresh garlic

1/4 cup minced onions

1 tbsp. freshly ground mustard seeds

1 tsp. powder or minced fresh ginger

1/4 fresh ground black pepper

1/4 tsp. salt or to taste

1/4 cup extra virgin olive oil

3 tablespoons lemon juice

3 cups of water

To be added before serving

1/4 cup cup red onion finely chopped

1 green bell pepper finely chopped

1 red bell pepper finely chopped

2 green onion stalks finely chopped

1 serrano pepper finely chopped

Preparation

1. Wash the lentils and add in a pot containing the 3 cups of water.

2. Aslo add the onions and garlic and cook for 20 minutes or until the lentils become soft. Remove from fire and let it cool down.

3. Remove from heat and let the mixture cool.

4. In a food processor add the lentil mixture, the ground mustard seeds, the black pepper, the lemon juice and the olive oil until all become smooth and soft.

5. Transfer from the food processor the now humus-like mixture into a bowl and add the red onions, green bell pepper, green onions and the serrano pepper. If you think it might be too spicey for you, add less of the serrano pepper.

6. Add salt to taste, mix well and serve.

My wife and I like to make it the way outlined above. Optionally, just mix everything without running them through the food processor. Make sure those items you chop are finely done.

Ingudai (mushroom) wot

Ingudai or mushrooms is one of the foods that were rarely consumed in the highlands of northwestern Ethiopia where I come from. I was intrigued the first time I ate mushroom wot at a friend's home in one of the towns I lived in. When I came to the United States, I was astounded to discover how prevalent mushrooms are . Just about every grocery store sells them and they are important part of the American diet—and for good reason. Mushrooms have many health benefits. They are rich in certain B vitamins, minerals and antioxidants. Good for the health of the cardiovascular system, the immune system and may also help prevent breast and pancreatic cancer.

Ingredients

1/2 cup of red onions

3 cups of mushrooms

3 cloves of garlic (finely minced)

1.5 cups green split peas

!/2 cup flax seeds flour

1/4 tbsp. fenugreek (abesh)

1/4 tsp. black pepper

1/4 cup berbere (or red pepper powder)

1/4 cup of extra virgin olive oil

1.5 tej or red wine

Salt to taste

Preparation

1. Boil the split peas in a pot with the 2 cups of water until soft and set aside

2. Add the onions and oil in a large frying pan and sauté until the onions turn light brown.

3. Add flax powder and fenugreek to the pan and stir and mix completely.

4. Add the berbere or red pepper powder, close pan and let it simmer in low heat. This makes the base sauce.

5. In a separate pan sauté the mushrooms for 3 minutes.

6. Add the peas, the mushrooms and the spices into the sauce and mix well.

7. Add the tej or wine and the remaining water into the mixture, close pan and cook at medium heat for 10 minutes.

8. Remove from fire and serve hot with injera or loaf. Store the leftover in the refrigerator for later consumption.

Duba (Pumpkin) Wot

In my birth village, we generally cut the duba into slices, cook in water and eat it with niter kebbeh and berbere. In the towns I lived, people often made a sauce out of duba, a welcome alternative to shiro wot, one of the most common sauces consumed. During fasting (when people abstain from meats and dairy products), duba wot becomes another vegetarian food.

Ingredients

5 cups of chopped and minced pumpkin (without the skin)

1 cup of chopped and minced red onions

1 tbsp. berbere or 3 medium size chili peppers

2 cloves of garlic, minced

3 tsp. of extra virgin olive oil

1 tsp. ginger (fresh or powder)

1/4 tsp. turmeric

1/2 tsp. black pepper

1/4 tsp. cumin powder

2 cups of water

Preparation

1. Remove the skin from the pumpkin, slice and dices them.
2. Sauté the onions in the oil untill they become light brown.
3. Add the water and the diced pumpkin and cook for 6-8 minutes.
4. Add the berbere, garlic, ginger powder and cumin and cook for 20 or so minutes. Add more water if needed.
5. Finally, add the black pepper, turmeric and cook 2-3 minutes more.
6. Make sure you cover the pot every time you let the sauce cook. The ingredients cook faster and you minimize water loss through evaporation.
7. Remove from fire and serve warm.

This recipe, like many others in this book, is very healthy as it contains beta-carotene (in the pumpkin and others), minerals and vitamins as well as anti-oxidants. Turmeric and black pepper have two well-known antioxidants. Black pepper increases the bioavailability of turmeric's antioxidant compounds in the body. That the two are included in this recipe is for this reason.

Buticha

I don't ever remember my mother preparing buticha when I lived in the country. I've had it in restaurants and at friends' homes in the towns I lived in. Buticha is one of those dishes most popular during the fast days. I'm including it here because I think it will be a nice optional dish for vegetarians like myself. It's also simple to prepare and the ingredients are commonplace.

Ingredients

1/2 cup of chickpea flour

1 tbsp. jalapeno pepper seeded and finely minced

1/2 cup minced onions

2 cloves of garlic

1 tsp. fresh or powder ginger

1/4 cup finely chopped green onion

1-3/4 cups of water

2 tbsp. extra virgin olive oil

1/4 tsp. turmeric

Preparation

1. Heat a medium size pan and sauté onions in the oil, till it turns brown.

2. Add garlic and ginger and saute for 1 minute.

3. Add 1/4 cup water and cook for 3 to 4 minutes.

4. Add the rest of the water, then the chickpeas flour and stir continously as the mixture simmer for 6 to 8 minutes.

5. Add the turmeric and jalapeno pepper and let it cook for 2-3 minutes.

6. Add the green onions and heat for 1 minute more.

7. Remove from fire, let it cool and serve.

Amli

This is a simpler shiro recipe. To distinguish it from the other shiro recipe in this book, I've christened it as Amli, the first two letters of my name and my wife's maiden name.

Ingredients

2 cups of water

1 cup of pea, chickpea or bean flour

4 cloves of garlic

2 tbsp. olive oil

1/2 tbsp. garlic salt to taste

Preparation

1. In a pan saute the garlic in the oil for 1 minute.

2. Add the water and the pea or chickpea or bean flour while stirring continuously.

3. Add the garlic salt and cook for 6 to 8 minutes

4. Add salt to taste and remove from fire and serve.

PART IV
Ethiopian Drinks

Ethiopian Drinks

An Introduction

There are a number of Ethiopian drinks and they are as unique as the foods and the culture—at least in the types of ingredients used and the way they are prepared. The most common traditional drinks are in the following chapters. However, considering there are over seventy different ethnic groups, one can expect to find more drinks and variations of the ones listed in this book throughout Ethiopia.

Tella, Tej and Areqey (also spelled Araqi or Araqe) are alcoholic beverages. As you will see, the difference among these three drinks is largely the ingredients used to make them and their alcohol content. The standard measure of the alcohol content in a beverage, ABV (Alcohol by Volume), is expressed as a percentage. See these at the end of the next chapter. Besides the traditional alcohol drinks, we also have their modern counter parts, produced in quantities and many varieties in commercial breweries, which I've included at the end of the same chapter. Then there are coffee and tea and juices of fruits and vegetables.

Chapter 21

Tella

A brown to dark brown alcoholic drink made from the following grain ingredients, gesho (the equivalent of hops) and herbs and spices in some cases. What I describe below represents how my mother from north-western Ethiopia used to prepare tella. As with the food recipes, traditionally there have not been standardized recipes and ways of preparation for any of the drinks. They are passed on from one generation to the next and the quality and alcohol content of each beverage can vary depending on the proportions and types of the ingredients used, and on the talent and skill of the makers.

Ingredients my mother used

Grain: barley, wheat, maize, teff, millet or sorghum. She used any one or two of these ingredients at a time.

Non-grain: gesho leaves and water

Brewing jar: thoroughly washed and rinsed with the juice of *gerawa* leaves and the interior smoked with burning sticks of *weyra* (similar to the olive tree or *tinjite* (a local plant) known as gembo. These treatments are both to impart flavor and sanitize the container.

Time: seven to twelve days or weeks sometimes

Preparations

There are no standardized measuring devices but the proportions are standard. A universal unit of measure, *eji*—hand is often used. For example 1 eji of gesho to 2 ejis of bikil and 10 ejis of kita. Eji (hand) can stand for a gram, a kilo gram or an ounce and a pound, to compare it to the western units of measure. The measuring devices can be *kuna*—a straw basket, clay pot or tumbler. The key here is the proportions. The women that brew these drinks know exactly what amount of each ingredient to use.

Often my mother also used her fingers, hands, keen sense of proportion and experience as her guides to create her beverage recipes as well as her culinary dishes. The outlines below come from my memory to a large extent. I've also consulted available references, just to make sure.

Making the *bikil*—malt

1. Soak a certain quantity of barely in water for three days. The amount will depend on whether my mother was making the tella for a big event—like a wedding, a holiday feast—or for regular household consumption.

2. Remove the water with a sieve a sieve. My mother used *wonfeet* or *kirchat*. The former is a straw basket with woven strings at the bottom, the latter, a laced bamboo basket.

3. Line a few round baskets with false banana leaves (here you can use aluminum foil or something similar) and transfer the wet barely into each basket, half full. With your hand or a spatula, push the grain out from the center to create a bowl-like cavity.

4. Cover completely each of the baskets and leave aside for 3 or 4 days so the grain germinates. Warm place can help it malt faster.

5. After the protracted time, remove the cover to find a tightly packed germinated grain called bikil in Amharic (also spelled as bekel).

6. Turn the baskets upside down to release the bowl-shaped bikil cakes.

You can break them apart and sundry them and follow the rest of the recipe.

My mother also used to mount the bikil cakes over the plunks of wood (*kott*) that spanned high over the open fire place in the living room. She left them there from a few days to several weeks, even months. The smoke from the fireplace can help enhance the aroma and flavor of the tella.

Gesho (*Rhamnus prinoides*, scientifically) is native to Ethiopia and a member of related species known as buckthorns. Its flowers are small and yellow with a tint of green in them. Its cherry-red berries are also small and often found tucked in the leaves. Nutritionally, they are rich in phytonutrients, vitamins, minerals and amino acids. In many African countries the berries are used as both food and medicine. In Ethiopia it's the leaves and stems that have greater value. They are used to make the local alcoholic beverages: tella (beer), tej (honey wine) and areqey (vodka).

Preparing the gesho and starting the brewing process

1. Sundry the leaves and stems. This done, pound them separately with mortar and pestle (shown below). Again, the amount of gesho you use will depend on the quantity of the beverage you plan to brew. Gesho is used mainly to give tella a tangy flavor, so you don't need a lot of it. See details below.

2. Mix the gesho powder and water in a relatively large container. For example, for a 3-gallon tella, my mother may have used 1-2 handfuls of the pulverized gesho leaves. Gesho is used mainly for flavor, to give the tella a tangy taste. So you don't need a lot of it.

3.Cover and let the mixture ferment for 3-4 days.

Wooden mortar and pestle

Making the kita from barley or other grains

1. Make a batter from ground millet (or barley) and bake into kita—thick flat bread.

2. When cooled break up into chunks or pieces and add a 10-eji or hand of it to the gesho-bikil mixture. Some places in Ethiopia women also add certain spices and herbs at this stage. I don't remember my mother adding anything else.

3. Close the jug and let it continue to ferment for 3 more days.

Asharo and Enkuro

The next ingredient(s) to be added to the brewing tella are *asharo*—roasted barley or corn and *enkuro*. For a tella that is being brewed for ten or fifteen days, just asharo is enough. On the other hand, if the tella is to age for a month or more, enkuro—heated ground wet corn or dagussa—is added. The corn kernels or the dagussa grains are germinated, dried and ground. Water is added to the flour, enough to wet it, then heated on a metal pan while continually stirring and mixing it until it becomes light brown to red. This is called Enkuro and is added to the fermenting tella along with the other ingredients, discussed below. Enkuro enhances the flavor of the aging tella as well as increase its volume.

Asharo

1. Roast 5 to 6 hands of barley or corn, till it becomes dark brown.
2. Remove from fire, cool down and grind.
3. Open the jug and add the asharo into the fermenting mixture. Here you also add a hand of the ground gesho sticks, more water and mix thoroughly.
4. Seal the jug and let it continue to brew for 3-4 days more. The longer it ferments, the more potent (relatively speaking), the alcoholic content of the tella will be. (The sealing in the countryside is done with mud.)

The final brew is a thick fusion called *difdif* in Amharic. You cut the difdif with water, filter and serve. How much water you add depends on how thick or strong you want the drink to be, 50/50 is generally good. The residue is called *atela* and is often given to cattle or other domestic animals.

As you will see below the alcohol content of tella is pretty low, compared with wine and spirits.

Note: the darker the kita and asharo, the darker will be the brewed tella. If light, the tella will have a yellowish hue. Since many of the ingredients are added in stages, you don't have to make them all at once. You make them following the phases of the brewing process.

The alcohol contents of different drinks

Drinks	% Alcohol
Tella	2.0 - 3.5
Tella, filtered	5.0 - 6.0
Tej	6.0 - 9.0
Areqey	22.0 - 28.0
Areqey, dagim	45.0 - 50.0

Source: Ethnomed: Author(s): Ruth Selinus from the Scandinavian Institute of African StudiesDate **Authored:** January 01, 1971

Modern Beers

1. **St. George** (lager), ABV: 4.5%, 33 cl
   Produced by BGI Ethiopia
   Strong and simple, good for a party

2. **Walia** (lager) ABV: 5%
   produced by HBSC, 33cl
   Has a unique aroma

3. **Castel** (Lager), ABV: 5.5%, 33cl
   Produced by BGI Ethiopia
   Smooth tasting

4. **Bedele** (Lager), ABV: 5.5%, 33cl
   Produced by Bedele Brewery
   Refreshing

5. **Dashen** (Pils), ABV: 4.5%, 33cl
   Produced by Dashen Brewery, Gondar

6. **Meta** (Lager), ABV: 5%, 33cl
   Produced by Meta ABO Brewery
   Sweet and tasty

7. **Meta Premium** (Lager), ABV: 5%, 33cl
   By Meta ABO Brewery S.C. Ethiopia
   Mature with a strong flavor

8. **Harar** (lager), ABV: 5%, 33cl
   By Harar Brewery, Ethiopia
   (Owned by HBSC)
   Bitter sweet with a bite

9. **Amber** (Lager), ABV: 5.5%, 33cl
   By BGI Ethiopia
   Sweet and spicy

10. **Hakim Stout** (Stout), ABV: 5.5%, 33cl
    By Harar Brewery, Ethiopia
    (Owned by HBSC)
    Aromatic, malty and slightly bitter

Chapter 22
Tej (Honey wine)

Tej is a wonderfully-tasting, gentle drink, akin to desert wine but the flavor and bouquet are distinctly its own. In the olden days, it was made and served in the royal households as well as in the homes of economically well-to-do families.

In Ethiopia the traditional tej is now largely sold in tej houses. The modern factory-made version is sold in restaurants and bars. In this country, you can find both versions in many Ethiopian restaurants. The ingredients are honey, gesho and time. Like all alcoholic beverages, it takes time and patience to prepare tej.

Just as with tella, I don't exactly remember what proportion of the ingredients my mother used to make tej. The general rule is use 1 part honey and 3 parts water in liquid volume. You add chopped twigs and sticks of gesho (not leaves). For example, for one gallon of tej, you would use a bundle of the gesho sticks.

Here is a recipe for all those who may want to try making tej at home.

Equipment:

- 1 gallon jar—a crock or glass carboy will do. If you use glass, make sure you cover it with something opaque (a blanket or dark plastic) to protect the mixture from strong light. A prolonged exposure to such light can oxidize certain molecules produced during fermentation.
- Gesho sticks or twigs (you can order them online or get them from a local Ethiopian market
- Long wooden spoon or some other stirrer
- Measuring cup
- Honey
- Water

Preparation

1. In the jug or carboy, mix 1 part honey and 3 parts of water. Stir well. This mixture is called *birz*. When an important guest arrives unannounced and the host has neither tella nor tej at home, she would quickly make birz to offer the guest. Plain water, unless the guest asks for it or she has no honey, is considered impolite.

2. Add a bundle or about 1/2 pound gesho stems

3. Cover the lead partially and sit tightly for two weeks

4. Within 3 to 4 days you should notice some activity

5. Open at the end of the first week, stir for a bit, close lead and let it continue to ferment.

6. On the second week bubbles form on top, showing increased conversion of the honey (sugar) into alcohol

7. Remove gesho sticks by filtration, stir well, close tightly and leave it untouched for the next 3 weeks.

8. In the fourth week, open jug, stir well, close and leave it till its final week of fermentation.

Chapter 23
Areqey

Commercially produced areqey

Areqey (also spelled Araqi or Araqe) is often made from the brew used for tella. In this case the alcohol is distilled and condensed along with the water. Home-distilling areqey is quite an elaborate process.

Equipment needed

- A large long necked jar called *gembo*. (See picture below.)
- A pint-size jar with a hole in its side, the size of a silver dollar
- A three-foot long bamboo pipe with a hole near one end
- A slender reed, the length of a woman's open hand
- An aluminum flask or similar metallic container
- A deep circular wooden or clay vat
- Thick rags, to wrap around the bamboo tube (shown)

Traditional areqey production set-up

The setup and procedure (as traditionally done)

1. Knead a mixture of earth, water, and fine straw and set it aside (used to seal the joints).

2. On three fireplace stones, balance the jug with its neck tipped down at an angle (as shown).

3. Transfer about two gallons of the concentrated *difdif* (see under tella above)—the fermented mixture—to the gembo, to distill it with a gallon of water.

4. Top the jug's opening with the little jar, its neck inserted into the gembo opening.

5. Insert one end of the bamboo tube into the hole in the side of the little jar.

6. Fit one end of the reed into the bored opening at the opposite end of bamboo tube.

7. Place the aluminum flask in the middle of the vat and secure it with granite slabs.

8. Move the vat under the end of the bamboo pipe and jiggle it until the attached reed lined up and dropped into the mouth of the flask.

9. Seal the gembo-jar and bamboo-reed-flask joints with the plaster of earth and straw mixture.

10. Smooth them with wetted hands the gembo-jar fixture on top, to resemble a freshly shaven woman's head.

Fill the vat with cold water and stoke the hearth under the jug by placing twigs and sticks through the gaps in the stones and light them with a match or torch.

It can take a major part of the twenty-four hours. The alcohol and water vapor percolate down the bamboo pipe and collect in the *kodda*—aluminum flask. However, you have to continue adding sticks to the fire, changing the vat water and cooling the pipe with an extra wet rag.

Distilling is a slow process. In twelve hours a woman can distill 3 to 4 times. At each set-up there are two different distillates. The first distillate that fills the kodda is called *kerari,* a relatively clear liquid. The second is called *sa'bia*, a cloudy-looking distillate.

The alcohol content of the kerari is higher than the sa'bia. If she distilled 3 times, adding new difdif each time, she will have 3 keraris and 3 sa'bias. In the 4th time, she could combine all the sa'bias and add them to a batch of difdif and distill them again. The resulting areqey is clearer and much stronger than the sa'bias or the kerari. A woman can also combine all the first batches (keraris) and distil them by themselves. The final areqey is called *dagim*—meaning distilled twice in Amharic and is equivalent to the commercially produced vodka, 90-100 proof.

Note: The clarity of the first batch will depend on the types of grains used. I don't remember which grain my mother used but I know some of her distillations came out clearer than others in the first run and she didn't have to reprocess them. Most women don't bother redistilling their areqey if it's for home consumption. If for sale, it's a different story. The areqey has to be clear enough for the buyer to see the sun when she puts up the areqey-containing bottle before her eyes. The residue of distillation is called *breent* and is often given to sheep and cattle.

Red areqey. Some women turn the dagim areqey by putting black tea leaves at the bottom of the receptacle kodda. When the kodda is removed and its content filtered, the redistilled areqey looks blood red.

I must add that despite the availability of these different alcoholic beverages, Ethiopians don't routinely drink alcohol. Libation if done with moderation is acceptable. Being under the influence of alcohol and losing one's self-control and dignity is frowned upon. *Sekaram*—drunk is the term used for someone who behaves wantonly; as if he was under the influence of alcohol.

Chapter 24
Coffee, Tea and Juices

Ethiopian coffee in *finjal*

Ethiopian tea in *birchiko*

Coffee

Coffee has historically been Ethiopia's economic mainstay. As mentioned earlier, this stimulant also was birthed in the country. It's no wonder then that Ethiopians drink coffee by the gallon (figuratively speaking) but by the small cups shown above, known as *finjal* (literally speaking).

For most Ethiopians, coffee is a social drink and the ritual is almost ceremonial in nature. You prepare coffee when a guest comes, during the religious holidays and to share a brew of it with the neighbors in the morning or on a leisurely afternoon. A person almost never roasts and makes coffee for herself or himself. People almost never keep pre-roasted, ground coffee at home. They roast it fresh and have to have somebody to enjoy the freshly brewed coffee with. This is what I meant by "social".

The same coffee in the pot is made three times. This is a must by convention. The first is called *abol*, the second *tona* and the third *bereka*. After the first batch, you add water to the residue and boil, remove from fire and serve. You do the same the third time. Without the addition of fresh coffee powder, the taste, aroma and strength progressively go down. For most attendants, it matters not. They are there to visit and drink the ritual three servings of coffee. I'm talking about the old rituals. Now things might have changed. People have no time to sit and wait for three servings.

Going back to the traditional habit, the stay after the first serving is to extend the visit or the conversation. Invariably, a snack of roasted barely, *kolo* or pea-size bread rolls, *dabo kolo*, are served. Nowadays popcorn can accompany the coffee drinking ceremony, particularly in the cities. The mouths of the visitors keep going on these foods as well as on the local politics or gossip.

During the holidays, pulpy grass called *ketema* is sprinkled on the floor and frankincense smokes by the entrance, adding aroma and texture to the coffee-making and drinking ceremony.

Coffee being poured into fingals   Frankincense smoking in a clay burner. You see the ketema in the background.

Tea

Although tea is native to Southeast Asia, it's now also cultivated in Ethiopia. However, the production is not high enough to make the country self-sufficient. Ethiopia still imports black tea and it's one of the most popular beverages in the homes and restaurants. The added spices make the Ethiopian tea particularly rich in aroma and flavor.

Tea recipe

The basic tea spices, as mentioned elsewhere in this book, are the green cardamom (pods), cloves and cinnamon sicks. If you want to venture out, you can add ginger (fresh) and nutmeg. For someone who is used to drinking tea with the standard spices, adding nutmeg and ginger doesn't make the taste the same. This is a matter of choice, of course . . . Incidentally, the tea is always the black variety. The recipe itself is pretty much a guesswork. You have try different proportion of the ingredients to get the right flavor. Remember this: cloves give the strongest flavor, then cardamum. Cinnamon has the mildest flavor of the three ingredients.

Here is more or less what my wife and I use for a four-cup tea recipe.
- 8 pods of green cardamum
- 10 heads of cloves
- 3 short sticks of cinnamon
- 2 bags of tea

Preparation

1. Add the cardamum, cloves and cinnamon sticks to 4-1/2 cups of water and bring it to a boil. Then reduce heat and let it simmer for 5 minutes
2. Drop the tea bags in a cup and add the hot spiced water. Steep the tea bag for 30 seconds. Then transfer and steep it in another cup of the spice water.

You can use honey or sugar to taste. My favorite Ethiopian tea used to be the one they boil the loose tea, the spices and sugar together. It was very good. I don't find many Ethiopian restaurant serving tea that way here in the United States. I think it's because sugar is a matter of taste and they don't want to be too presumptuous and offer such a tea to their customers. Even us, we often find ourselves steeping the tea bags instead of buying loose teas and boiling them together with the other ingredients.

Enjoy!

Juices

In the highlands where I come from, there were no fruit trees. I grew up not knowing even their existence. They didn't sell them in the markets either. In the lowlands *lomi-* (lemmon-), *birtukan-* (orange-), *kok-*(peach), *mooz-* (banana-), mango-(mango-), mandarin (mandarin), *ananas* (pine apple), *hopi* (passion fruit), *Roman-*(Roman Pomegranate), *abukado* (avocado), *beles-/shola-* (fig-), *zeytoni-* (guava-), apple-(apple-) trees grow. People ate these fruits straight as well as made them into drinks, often combining them in layers, creating an eye-catching patterns. *Weyn* (grape) also grows in the warmer climates. It's used during church ceremonies as well as for making wine, *weyn tej*.

In the highlands as well as in the flatter and warmer climates, enjori (strawberries, two varieties—one, similar to the black berries here but lighter in color, another, bigger and tube-like with tapering end, which shows a gaping opening when you detach it from the vine, orange-ish in color). There was one particular fruit trees called qega (which bears fleshy, apricot-color fruit with small white seeds in it) that I remember but never seen it anywhere else. We enjoyed the drink we made from it. The same thing with the strawberries.

Below are examples of some of the fruit juices. Traditionally, the drinking cups are clay tumblers called *tiwa* or horn cups known as *wancha*. The elegant glasses below are the modern, factory-made, versions.

PART V
Appendices

APPENDIX A
Free Radicals and Antioxidants

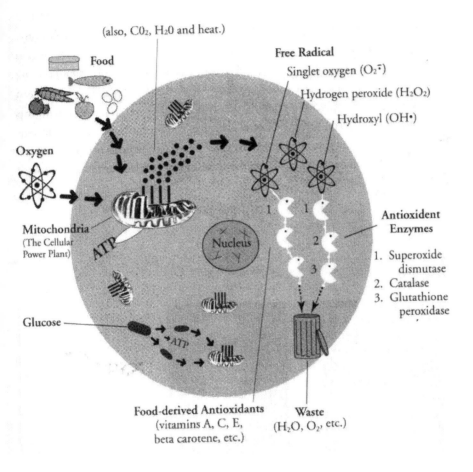

Figure A.1 Free Radical Generation and Cellular Energy Production

Within this orb lies everything that you are or are able to do.

Free Radicals

Atoms are the basic building blocks of any substance. When atoms combine, they form stable molecules, like oxygen in our atmosphere (two oxygen atoms combined as one molecule) or water (two hydrogen atoms and one oxygen atom). When certain molecules combine, they form long chain substances (or polymers) like proteins, fats and carbohydrates—just to name a few.

Atoms or molecules are bonded together by electrons. In organic compounds, the most frequent number of electrons shared between atoms is two. These bonds are not permanent. Depending on the presence of other forces (temperature, radiation and chemical agents), these bonds can break and separate from each other, leading to an uneven number of electrons in each molecule or atom. As shown in Figure A1, the same situation can result when a molecule is stripped off one of its outer electrons. In either case, the resulting molecule or atom is referred to as a free radical. In the body, free radicals are generated during the normal course of metabolism, or they may be induced by environmental factors, such as radiation and pollution.

Free radicals are unstable substances that cause havoc in the area in which they roam or with the things they encounter. A free radical's ultimate goal is to find another atom or molecule with which to pair up or from which to steal an electron to become stable again. When this happens, however, new free radicals are formed that go around attacking more molecules to generate still more free radicals. Such a chain reaction could millions of free radicals. If this reaction goes unchecked, it can lead to major complications in the body.

Cell membranes are damaged. Collagen and elastin proteins cross-link, causing wrinkles or lines to form in the skin. Fats become rancid. Contacts between nerve cells are severed, and the DNA malfunctions. The cumulative effect is physical and mental aging, as well as the onset of various degenerative diseases like cancer, stroke, arthritis, arteriosclerosis, diabetes and senility.

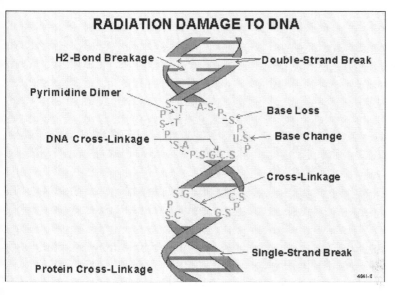

Figure A.2 A Free Radical Damaged DNA. Like moths that shred your wool clothes to pieces or termites that gnaw away the inner workings of your house, uncontrolled free radicals can do the same to your genes and delicate tissues of your body.

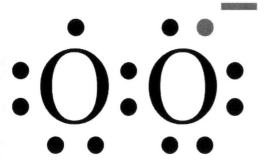

Superoxide (02, • —)

This oxygen molecule known as superoxide radical is missing one electron. One of the by-products of metabolic processes, superoxide free radical is very unstable and dangerous to the body tissues.

Figure A.3 An Illustration of a Free Radical

Missing electron (free radical) attacks any double bond such as in the fatty acids of intracellular membranes, DNA and other molecules.

Sources of Free Radicals

Inside the body, free radicals can be generated from normal metabolic processes and by white blood cells, which use them as a weapon to kill disease-causing foreign elements in the body. They can also be generated by oxidation of unsaturated fats, such as those found in the brain and other parts of the body.

Some of the environmental sources of free radicals are x-rays, ultraviolet light, chemical toxins in the air and water (such as lead, cadmium, mercury, copper and even iron) and nuclear radiation.

Cigarette smoking and dietary fats and oils—particularly those oils processed by the heat extraction method—are other common sources of free radicals. Barbecued and fried foods, such as those you buy at fast-food outlets, are also a great source of free radicals. The combination of high-temperature heated oils (used to prepare these foods) and oxygen is the ideal condition for the generation of enormous numbers of free radicals. The high temperature at the burning tips of cigarettes and the tar that results are also major sources of free radicals.

A single puff of cigarette smoke, for example, can contain up to 100 trillion free radicals, never mind the 3000 plus different aromatic compounds some of which are known carcinogens, it contains.

Perhaps the greatest source of free radicals is the oxygen we consume every day. It's reported that for every 25 molecules of oxygen we inhale, 1 free radical is produced. Considering that we consume trillions of oxygen molecules, with a single gulp of air, you can imagine how many free radicals can be generated every time you breathe in air.

In the mitochondria, during food metabolism, oxygen is reduced to water and carbon dioxide through an addition of electrons one at a time. Hence addition of one electron to a food-derived molecule generates the superoxide free radical (shown in Figure A.3) two electrons, the hydrogen peroxide free radical, and four electrons, water molecules. In the presence of energy such as UV light, x-ray, iron and copper the hydrogen peroxide converts to the hydroxyl free radical which is the most noxious of the radicals formed in the body. Hydrogen peroxide and hydroxyl free radicals are shown in Figure A.1).

It is important to note that free radical generation takes place throughout a person's lifetime but increases with age. Particularly vulnerable are brain cells and white blood cells because they are rich in unsaturated fats. A destruction of large numbers of white blood cells can lead to the weakening of your immune system. This is one of the reasons why you become more susceptible to diseases and infections as you get older.

Antioxidants

Luckily, we are not entirely without defense against these freaks of nature, free radicals. Through our bodies' manufacture of its own antioxidant enzymes and by the food we eat, we can help shield our tissues and organs from free radical damage. The three most powerful antioxidant enzymes are superoxide dismutase (SOD), glutathione peroxidase and catalase. These enzymes are manufactured by the body to promote good health.

Superoxide dismutase specifically works to help fight oxygen free radicals. Our body burns the food we eat by using oxygen through a process called metabolism. During this process, many oxygen free radicals are produced, the most common one being the superoxide free radical (see Figure A.3). The SOD helps neutralize this free radical before it attacks tissues and begins a chain reaction.

What is interesting is that there are two types of SOD—one that exists inside the mitochondria of the cell, the other outside but within the cell. The one inside the mitochondria has manganese as its component, and the one outside has zinc and copper in its structure. It has been shown that a small deficiency in any of these elements greatly affects the SOD activity in our body, thus speeding up our cellular attack by free radicals and our biological aging.

The minerals zinc, copper and manganese aid the body to manufacture its own SOD. Similarly, catalase is an antioxidant enzyme that is formed with and activated by iron. In collaboration with the other enzymes, it helps neutralize free radicals generated in the cell. Its function is primarily to neutralize the hydrogen peroxides.

The other antioxidant enzyme, glutathione peroxidase, is a very versatile molecule involved in a variety of activities in the body. This enzyme promotes the effectiveness of Vitamin C and Vitamin E and enhances the immune system. Glutathione peroxidase can also help neutralize the unhealthy effects of heavy metals such as cadmium, mercury, lead and aluminum. It saves cells from oxidation. Both white and red blood cells depend on this enzyme for their proper functioning. The power behind glutathione peroxidase comes from the mineral selenium, which is one of the major components of the enzyme.

Food-Derived Antioxidants

There are many well-documented antioxidants obtained from the food you eat. Some of the prominent ones are Vitamins A, C and E, beta carotene, minerals such as selenium, copper, zinc, manganese and iron, glutathione and the amino acids cysteine, methionine and lysine. And then you have the phytochemicals, as discussed on Page 105, found in many types of vegetables and fruits and the herbs and spices. As mentioned there, each one of these nutrients has many benefits to our health besides its role as an antioxidant. Let's look at each one separately.

Beta Carotene—Precursor of Vitamin A

"Eat your carrots. They can help you see better at night." Perhaps you heard your mother chirp this when you were little. And from that time on you have associated the absence of carrots in your diet with night blindness. You try to include a few sticks of these tuberous vegetables whenever you get a chance.

Perhaps you now know that carrots are good for you because they contain a substance known as beta carotene. It is beta carotene that converts to Vitamin A in the body and helps the *visual purple*—the pigment in the retina that enables your eyes to quickly adapt when you go from light to darkness.

For a long time, scientists had associated Vitamin A with night vision. Vitamin A is now known, however, to have many different functions and benefits for the human body. One of these functions is fighting free radicals. In the body the two most common free radicals are those that form from oxygen molecules and poly-unsaturated fatty acids (PUFAs). PUFAs are an integral part of the cell membrane, body fat and some of the food you eat. Beta carotene is known to be an excellent scavenger of the PUFA-generated and singlet oxygen free radicals. Singlet oxygen free radical is one of the most damaging of the oxygen radicals in the body.

In test experiments, Vitamin A was also found to inhibit chemically induced cells from becoming cancerous. This, in itself, is very important because our body is constantly exposed to all kinds of chemical carcinogens found in foods as additives, e.g., preservatives, coloring and flavoring agents and texturizers. Vitamin A can also help fight the cancerous effect of drugs, cigarettes, radiation, water and air pollutants.

Vitamin C

Unlike vitamins A and E (the fat-soluble antioxidants), Vitamin C has the distinct advantage of being water soluble. Since nearly two-thirds of our body is water, it means this vitamin can go just about anywhere in the body. As an antioxidant, Vitamin C can travel freely in the bloodstream and aid the cells and tissues from the effects of free radicals.

Vitamin C, in effect, acts as your body's sacrificial lamb. A Vitamin C molecule gives up one of its electrons to a free radical substance, and in so doing, self-destructs. This battle between Vitamin C and free radicals takes place thousands, if not millions, of times a second (depending on the number of free radicals present in your body and the Vitamin C level in your bloodstream).

Free radicals, besides contributing to your aging process, are responsible for a variety of cancers. Vitamin C, by neutralizing these marauding chemical species and by boosting your immune forces (antibodies, white blood cells, lymphocytes), protects your body from bacterial and viral infections as well as from cancerous growth. In addition, Vitamin C is known to block the formation of nitrosamines—cancer-initiating compounds formed from proteins and nitrites (such as sodium nitrite), which are used as food preservatives.

Vitamin E

Vitamin E is the other food-based antioxidant that has important functions in the body. As one of the few fat-soluble vitamins, vitamin E's primary function is to protect fat molecules from free radical attack. These include the triglycerides and cholesterol in the circulatory blood and the polyunsaturated fats (PUFs) found in the cell membranes and the brain cells.

As said earlier, free radicals are generated during a normal metabolic process or are imported from outside via the water and foods we consume. These ravaging chemical species attack everything they encounter, but they have an affinity for the fundamental building units of your tissues and organs: the cells. A significant portion of the membrane that covers the cells and the sheath that coats nerve axons is made from proteins and substances known as polyunsaturated fatty acids (PUFAs).

As mentioned above, PUFAs are highly vulnerable to a free radical attack. Vitamin E is one of the few fat-soluble vitamins and lodges itself in the membranes of the cells and neutralizes the free radicals before they harm the membrane substances. In doing so, this vitamin averts the onset of many diseases and premature aging.

This effect of Vitamin E has been shown in several experiments. Researchers in one study showed the protective level of Vitamin E by giving a group of people 600 I.U. of the vitamin for ten days and then subjecting their red blood cells to oxygen and light. When they compared these results with that of the control group (those who had not received vitamin E), the red blood cells from the group who were supplemented with Vitamin E oxidized by only 8% while those of the control group were completely destroyed.

In another experiment, rats supplemented with Vitamin E had a greater resistance to the damaging effects of lead poison than those that weren't given the vitamin. Vitamin E in collaboration with Vitamin C has also been shown to counter the cancerous effects of several food additives (such as sodium nitrite) that lead to the formation of nitrosamines-well-known carcinogens. Nitrogen dioxide, a common pollutant and byproduct of automobile exhaust, is also known to be damaging to the lungs. There is evidence to show that vitamins C and E help prevent this problem, too.

The Mineral Antioxidants

The antioxidant property of the minerals copper, zinc, manganese, iron and selenium has largely to do to their function as part of the enzymes systems discussed earlier. Copper, zinc and manganese are part of the two superoxide dismutases that neutralize the superoxide free radical produced from the consumption of oxygen. Iron and selenium, as partners of catalase and glutathione peroxidase, respectively, help in destroying the hydrogen peroxide free radicals as well as free radicals generated from the breakdown of fats. Of course, as discussed in their respective sections, these minerals have many other functions and benefits to the body besides their antioxidant properties.

Selenium

Selenium has many great benefits to your health. As an antioxidant, selenium can function by itself or in conjunction with the enzyme glutathione peroxidase, a powerful enzyme that plays many important functions in the body, including fighting free radicals, boosting the immune system, cancer prevention and detoxification of heavy metals (such as cadmium, mercury, lead, arsenic) from the body. The mineral selenium is an integral part of this enzyme. Each molecule of the enzyme cradles four atoms of selenium. Many of the metabolic free radical fragments, such as hydrogen peroxides, and those generated from the breakdown of fats are neutralized with the help of this enzyme.

Selenium, together with vitamin E, has also been shown to fight the onset of two major killers: heart disease and cancer, so much so that the incidence of these diseases and the level of selenium in the soil have been correlated. In the areas of the country where there is a low level of selenium in the soil, there are more deaths from cancer and heart disease.

This amazing mineral has many other benefits. The prevalence of cancer, for example, is equally consistent with the level and geographical distribution of selenium around the world. According to studies from many different countries, the use of selenium in the diet helps minimize the incidence of several types of cancer, including breast, uterine, lung, pancreatic, rectal, mouth, prostate, lymph gland, liver, thyroid, colonic and ovarian cancer. Selenium was found to be equally effective against cancer of the bladder, skin, cervix, esophagus, intestine, pharynx and kidneys.

Interestingly, even those who have already succumbed to cancer seem to realize improved survival time, fewer malignancies or metastases and less recurrence of lesions when they received sufficient selenium.

A study in which mice were infected with a virus that induces mammary cancer showed a reduction by eightfold in the occurrence of the tumor with a selenium-containing diet. This is a dramatic improvement considering that these mice ordinarily develop tumors in a purported 95% to 100% of the time when infected with the same virus.

Because of the close similarity to the way breast cancer develops in humans, the scientist who did the above study feels that the incidence of breast cancer in this country would be reduced significantly if women took 250 to 350 micrograms of selenium supplements daily.

Selenium is also very important for the proper functioning of the sex organs. The production of sperm cells, as well as their strength and motility, is aided by the level of selenium in these organs. More than half of the body's selenium is found in the testicles and seminal ducts. This means that every time men have sex, they lose a fair amount of it. To maintain an adequate body level of this mineral, they have to keep replenishing it.

In other areas, selenium has been found to be beneficial in the efficient production of energy, in relieving arthritis and in reducing the incidence of cataracts. All these, incidentally, have something to do with selenium's ability to fight free radicals.

Selenium is, indeed, a remarkable mineral.

Cysteine, Glutathione, Methionine and Lysine

In addition to vitamins and the mineral selenium, there is a group of amino acids that are well-known antioxidants. Glutathione is a small peptide molecule consisting of glutamic acid, cysteine and glycine.

Glutathione helps in the synthesis of the enzyme glutathione peroxidase. This enzyme, as was discussed earlier, has many protective benefits in your body. Glutathione, in collaboration with selenium, helps fight free radicals, guards against cirrhosis of the liver, boosts the protective power of vitamins E and C, assists in removing toxic metals from the system and helps in the production and fortification of immune cells.

Cysteine and methionine are the two sulfur-containing amino acids that are known to be good antioxidants. These amino acids, besides functioning as building components for the regeneration of tissues, are great at mopping up accumulated toxins, such as metabolic by-products, tobacco and alcohol derivatives and heavy metals, such as mercury, lead and cadmium, from the body.

All these are deleterious to the body's organs and tissues. Lysine is known to help boost the immune system by encouraging the production of antibodies. In addition, a daily dose of 1,000 mgs of lysine was shown to reduce herpes breakout in those who carry the virus.

Herbal Antioxidants

Over many years now, the phytochemicals or phytonutrients have been toted, after vitamins, as the next group of substances that may have many beneficial properties in our health. These compounds, which are extracted from the green, red, blue, black and yellow of vegetables and fruits, are not exactly nutrients (at least so far as we know), in the sense that they don't get involved in energy production or in repairing and building of tissues, but they apparently have many influences in the health and wellness of our bodies. One of these influences is in serving as antioxidants. The other is by interacting or interfering with certain enzymes and substances in our tissues in ways that enhance and maintain the health and well-being of our bodies.

Some of these compounds are sulforaphane (from broccoli), lycopene (from tomatoes), lutein (from alfalfa), allylic sulfides (from garlic), genistein (from soybeans) and capsaicin (from red peppers). There are many other compounds found in different herbs and spices that have been shown to have beneficial properties in our bodies. (Read the information on phytochemicals and herbal antioxidants).

A Team of Antioxidants for Maximum Health

If you notice, in a well-formulated supplement, all antioxidant vitamins, minerals and phytonutrients appear together. There are reasons for this:

1. All the antioxidants do not necessarily have the same function; that is to say, certain antioxidants are more effective than others in neutralizing certain types of free radicals. For example, beta carotene and selenium (as part of the enzyme glutathione peroxidase) are more powerful neutralizers of the singlet oxygen free radicals. This means, for instance, that during a strenuous physical exertion, like exercise or physical labor, you tend to use up a higher volume of oxygen, which consequently increases the metabolic activities of your cells and the production of the singlet oxygen free radicals. Taking the recommended amounts of these nutrients prior to your physical activity can thus minimize the damage these radicals can cause.

Vitamin E and selenium, on the other hand, are great suppressors of fat peroxidation. Fat peroxidation (the rupturing of fat molecules leading to the formation of free radicals) can be initiated by a number of agents, including radiation, toxic metals and chemicals, singlet oxygen free radicals and a number of other substances. Tissues that are highly vulnerable to some of these agents are the lungs, the digestive tract and the liver.

As you must know, the lungs and the digestive tract are the primary contacts of everything that enters the body, including the various chemicals and pollutants that come along with food, water and air. The liver, besides serving as main distribution center, is the place where many of the body's toxins accumulate. Consequently, these three organs take the brunt of many of the effects posed by substances that come in from outside as well as by those generated from within the body. The vitamins E and C and the mineral selenium are known to be excellent protectors of these tissues.

The phytoantioxidants also have their own special functions in the body. Some of them activate enzymes that are intimately involved in the health and proper function of the cell. Hence, for instance, while sulforaphane induces the synthesis of enzymes that are closely involved with the proper function of the cells, others like coumaric acid and cholorogenic acid help remove unfriendly substances from them. There are also phytoantioxidants involved in the health of certain tissues of the body. For example, the anthocyanosides (in bilberry) help with the health of the retina, and leucoanthocyanin (in grape seed extract) is important for the well-being of the blood capillaries. Likewise, the flavonoid molecules found in ginkgo biloba are important for the health and proper function of the brain and circulatory system.

2.   When antioxidants are present together, besides enhancing your issues, they protect one another and other nutrients from the effects of the free radicals. For instance, Vitamin A protects vitamin C, which, in turn, protects vitamins A and E and some of the B complex vitamins from free radicals or other oxidative process. Vitamin E, similarly, can serve as a "bodyguard" for vitamins C, D and F[2] and the B complex vitamins.

As you can see, you should have not only high concentrations of the antioxidants in your tissues but also all of them together so that each one will adequately complete its specific job without getting destroyed before it reaches its destination—usually the cells. As an illustration, think of military airplanes that are on a bombing mission. Unless these planes are adequately shielded from enemy air fire by an escorting aircraft, they may never reach their target.

Inside your body, at a microcosmic level, a raging battle goes on between the free radicals and antioxidants. As in the real world, who wins this battle depends on the number and strength of the forces involved.

---

2   Essential fatty acids like omega-3 and omega-6 fatty acids.

APPENDIX B
The Importance of Good, Clean Water to Your Health and Longevity

Throughout this book, we have talked about how good nutrition is the basis of good health, well-being and longevity. Good, clean water is an integral part of good health and nutrition. In fact, considering that about two-thirds of your body consists of water and that water is the medium in which nearly all the metabolic processes take place, the quality or integrity of this medium is very important indeed.

Some of the degenerative diseases such as cancer, arthritis, atherosclerosis (hardening of the arteries), kidney stones, cataracts, hearing loss, diabetes and a number of others that come with age could be caused by a lifelong consumption of bad water, as much as by bad nutrition. Unfortunately, as long as the water we use or drink every day satisfies our thirst, tastes reasonably OK and is readily available, many of us don't think twice about it.

In reality, as you can see below, the water you use from your tap, well or river can be the harbinger of many health hazards. These health problems are not cholera, typhoid, dysentery or any number of other water-borne diseases that have caused devastations in various parts of the world throughout history. The modern versions of these once fatal diseases are subtle, and in most cases, causes and symptoms may not be directly correlated. This is because many of the maladies that can be attributed to pollutants in water can also come from other sources.

From a number of disease-causing chemicals that are often found in our drinking waters and from the continuous rise in many degenerative diseases, as well as from specific correlational findings[3], our drinking water has indeed come to be a growing threat to our health. For example, radioactive minerals such as strontium 90, radium 226 and 228 and common chemicals such as chlorides and nitrates are known to be carcinogens. Yet all these and many other substances can commonly be found in our drinking water, albeit some in tolerable amounts.

The Environmental Protection Agency (EPA) has called the water pollution problem "the most grievous error in judgment we as a nation have ever made." Dr. Patrick Quillin, in his book *Healing Nutrients*, writes that those who still drink normal tap water are either "uniquely blessed with an isolated pocket of clean water" or "very cavalier about (their) health."

What Could Be Wrong With Your Drinking Water

Besides the inorganic minerals that naturally abound in most ground and river waters, there can be countless chemicals, bacteria, viruses and even radioactive stances contained in the water you use every day. Some of these pollutants come from agricultural runoffs. These can be pesticides, herbicides and fungicides, and fertilizers such as nitrates, sulfates and chlorides. Industrial and power plants emit a lot of waste (which includes radioactive substances) into the atmosphere and the water supply above or under the ground. Similarly, hydrocarbons and pollutants from auto exhaust fumes can find their way into the lakes, rivers and reservoirs from which your city draws your drinking water.

Moreover, because water is highly mobile and interactive (many organic and inorganic chemicals can dissolve in it), the pollutants that may exist in your drinking water may have come from far away. Because of this and the above reasons, the quality of the water you use for consumption should be of paramount importance[4]. Unfortunately, most of us are indeed cavalier about our drinking water. The sad thing about it is that our water pollution problem is not getting better. One writer refers to this worsening situation as a "scourge of major proportion (that could become) our legacy."

---

3   For example, people who live in New Orleans, near the delta of the Mississippi River are found to have a higher incidence of kidney and bladder cancers, as well as other urinary tract disorder. Nitrates from farmland runoffs that often contaminate the water supply in the Midwest, are probable culprits, and are known to be a major health hazard to babies and adults alike."

4   Even in a situation in which the quality of the water is closely monitored, the allowable level for each contaminant has been determined without the availability of studies of their long-term, chronic ingestion even at these "low" levels.

Here is a list of some of the substances that can be found in your drinking water:

- EDBs
- Strontium 90
- Algae
- Thorium
- Tannins
- Magnesium
- Petroleum solvents
- Copper
- Benzene
- Cadmium
- Nitrates
- Rust particles
- Chlorides
- Nickel

- Zinc
- Bacteria
- Silver
- Aluminum
- Mercury
- Pesticide
- Iron
- THMs
- Calcium
- Sulfates
- Arsenic
- Chlorine
- Sand
- Carbon 14

- Viruses
- Sodium
- Lithium
- Radium 226 & 228
- Herbicides
- Lead
- PCBs
- Chromium
- Sulfides
- Barium
- Fluorides
- Silt
- Cesium 137
- Radon

Because of these and many other inorganic and organic substances, your water can sometimes look unappetizingly murky, taste heavy and muddy and smell stale and swampy.

The heavy metals—cadmium, lead, mercury and others from the list above also known to generate free radicals, those chemical renegades that create havoc in chlorinated chemicals can generate free radicals on their upon by the enzymes in your body or can combine with water, hydrogen peroxide and hypochlorite (a compound found in most make the dangerous singlet oxygen free radicals. These chemical species, as mentioned, earlier, are believed to be one of the causes cancer.

Similarly, nitrates are a problem because when they combine with the amino acids in your diet, they create nitrosamines—also well-known carcinogens. Then have you have the radioactive elements such as carbon 14, strontium 90, radon and thorium that can collect in the bones to become a health threat. As you probably know, radioactive materials are carcinogenic as well.

Contrary to popular belief, the inorganic minerals such as calcium and magnesium that you find in most drinking waters may actually have a negative impact on your health. Some of these minerals, for example calcium, can settle out in the arterial walls, causing them to harden, collect cholesterol and impede the normal blood flow. The technical term for this is atherosclerosis, which is one of the causes of heart attacks and stroke. The reason why they can be bad when found in water but good when found in food or nutritional supplements is discussed further on in this section.

Minerals can also collect in the joints, kidneys, pancreas and inner ears, as well as eyes and tissues, leading to arthritis, kidney failure, diabetes, hearing loss and cataracts. According to Dr. Allen Banik, because of the impact they have on many vital functions of the body, too many minerals in your drinking water can "destroy every fond hope you have by striking you down . . . and will draw your activities from the great out-of-doors, into creaking rocking chairs and finally into bedridden old people's homes."

Considering how important minerals are to our health, the above statements may come as a total surprise to you. Minerals are very, be very important. Among other things, your muscles, heart, brain and many other body processes depend on minerals for their proper functioning. You need, however, only the minerals you get from organic sources, from the food you eat or from supplements.

Studies have shown that the amount of minerals the body metabolizes from drinking water (whether it be mineral, tap or well water) is less than 5%. And according to the American Medical Journal, "the body's need for minerals is largely met through foods, not drinking water." Similarly the National Water Quality Association has remarked: "The amounts of minerals found in water are insignificant when compared to those found in the food we eat."

To understand how waterborne minerals behave in your body, you can think of a river that carries sand, silt and many other organic and inorganic matters in it. This river, as it flows from higher grounds to the lower, flat lands, leaves behind much of what it carries along its course, banks and delta. Over a period of time, a lot of the material could collect so high and wide that it could cause the river to divert its course.

The blood in your arteries is similar to such a river in that it, too, tends to deposit any excess material along its path until, after some point, the sludge of minerals and fat harden and begin to interfere with the normal flow of blood. In your body, excess cholesterol, fat and mineral sedimentation are some of the major causes of circulatory disorders.

Amazingly, the average person could consume roughly 450 pounds of inorganic minerals from tap and well water in his/her lifetime. Where do you think some of this gunk ends up? Your kidneys try to get rid of as much as they can. What's left may slowly accumulate in the blood vessels, joints, lungs and other tissues in your body, leading to some of the diseases that come with age.

The Solution

Your best solution is to drink pure water, free of any of these substances. This means distilled water. Distillation, in combination with pre-carbon filtration, give you water that is 99.9% pure. Despite popular belief, this is the kind of water that is ideal for drinking. Your food and supplements, not your drinking water that can provide you with the minerals your body needs.

Reverse osmosis (RO) is perhaps the next best method of water purification. Manufacturers of RO systems claim that their devices can remove anywhere from 85% to 95% of substances found in water, but these percentages go down over time. Some critics have put the figures as low as 50% to 70% after a few operations. In either case, RO filters seem to have more problems than the manufacturer or door-to-door RO water filter salesperson would be willing to admit to.

Such problems include quality, variability in the filtered water, short service of the membrane, carbon and sediment filters (lasting only 1 to 2 years) water wasting. With steam distillers, you have none of these problems.

Let's now see how the city purifies the water you drink daily. The most common methods of water purification (carbon filtration and sediment filtration) remove only 20% and 5%, respectively, of matter contained in water. These two methods are used by most cities and towns to bring you filtered drinking water.

Depending on where you live and the type of water (soft or hard, lake or river or ground water) that exists there, your city may use different treatments and filtration process. Most of these treatments are designed to make the water safe (free of disease-causing bacteria and viruses) and to reduce unwanted smell, taste and appearance.

In typical filtration, a combination of several processes may be used. For starters, long-term storage is used to settle much of the suspended matter and bacteria.

This may be followed by aeration to reduce taste and odor and by coagulation and sedimentation to enhance the color and lower the material content. Because coagulation often entails the addition of several chemicals, such as ferrous sulfate, lime, sodium aluminate and ferric chloride, the resulting water can become hard and corrosive.

The last three steps of purification involve softening, filtration and disinfection. The softening process uses ion-exchange resins to remove most of the calcium and magnesium. The filtration process can be accomplished using either fine sand, underlaid with gravel or just large grains of sand. Both of these processes are used to improve the appearance as well as to reduce the mineral and bacterial content of the water. The final stage of the purification involves disinfection. This step most commonly uses chlorine, but ozone and ultraviolet radiation are also used to kill bacteria and to disable viruses. In addition, copper sulfate, to control algae growth, and activated charcoal, to trap odor and organic chemicals, may be used.

After all these steps, the maximum your town's filtration systems can do is to remove only up to 25% of the substances contained in your drinking water. This means that from the list of substances you saw earlier, the sediment filtration stage removes mainly sand, silt and rust particles, while the others and the activated carbon filter help remove bacteria and organic substances such as benzene, THMs, PCBs, petroleum solvents and some of the pesticides and herbicides. The activated carbon filtration can also remove bad taste, odors and chlorine. Otherwise, nearly 75% of what you see on the list, if they already exist in the water being processed, can end up in your tap water.

The other problem, often not apparent to the average consumer, is old, corroding water pipes. In fact, your city's water purification centers may have done the best they could in filtering your water supply. What they often don't have control over are the leaching metals such as copper, lead, nickel, cadmium and others that may be found in the network of underground water pipes.

Depending on the condition of the water itself (acidic or basic), the duration of contact it has had with the pipes since it left its source and the age of the pipes, you could have various levels of leaching and contaminations as a result of the above metals. For instance, a significant level of leached copper can change the appearance of your water to blue. A high level of lead in drinking water can cause a number of physical and neurological disorders, particularly in children. It can affect a child's mental development and learning abilities. The heavy metals listed also are known to be free radical generators, as we said in earlier chapters, and can initiate a number of diseases and speed up aging. To deal with these problems, you have a few choices.

The first option is to purchase distilled water for drinking and cooking. It may cost you considerably less than what you ordinarily pay for bottled water.

The second option is to buy and install your own steam distillation or reverse osmosis system. A distillation system, as we said earlier, is the best. You consistently get top quality water, and the system can last you a long time compared to an RO system. If this is too expensive, find a water company that at least uses reverse osmosis and purchase your water from it. In the long run, though, you might be better off owning a purification system.

The third option is to use tap water cautiously. If your piped water has not been in use for some time, such as overnight or when you've been on vacation, turn the faucet on and let the water run for at least 3 to 5 minutes. This will help flush any accumulated leached-out minerals in the water.

If you depend exclusively on your tap or even bottled and spring water for your drinking and cooking, eat foods that are a good source of antioxidants. Vitamin A, for instance, as retinol or beta carotene, is a great neutralizer of singlet oxygen free radicals. So are selenium and vitamin E. As mentioned earlier, singlet oxygen free radicals are some of the commonly produced chemical species in the presence of salt, sodium, chlorine and water.

Vitamin C and the amino acids cysteine and methionine are good in removing many of the toxic metals that may exist in your drinking water." Best of all, make your Four Pillars drink and consume it with all your meals. For the times you have not made the drink and as an added protection , find a good multi-vitamin supplement and take it regularly.

In summary, your overall health will greatly depend on both good nutrition and the quality of the water you drink. Since water occupies the largest volume in your body and since the multitude of biochemical processes that takes place in it happen in a water medium, the purity or integrity of this medium is very important for the efficiency and consistency of these processes.

Because polluted drinking water tends to depress your immune system, replacing your water supply with pure water will help you feel healthier and stronger.

When your body fluids are "uncluttered (as they are when you drink pure water), hormones can zip around the body quicker, oxygen and nutrients are transported faster and the enzymes and other chemicals work with higher efficiency. All these, in turn, can make you feel healthier and stronger. Pure water is truly a gift of nature. And you should give it to your body every day.

APPENDIX C
The Importance of Physical Exercise

Understanding Exercise

This book cannot be complete without including a section on exercise. Physical exercise is a spice of life. Just as food can be pretty bland, dull and boring, life without regular exercise can be equally dull and boring. It's not food, it's not water, and your body doesn't depend on it for its survival. Yet, for those who want to live longer and look and feel better and younger, exercise can make a world of difference in their health. It's the last piece in the puzzle that completes and optimizes one's picture of health.

Perhaps the first and immediate benefit of exercise is that it can help you release stress, depression and any other matters that may be clouding your mind at the time. Exercise heightens your awareness of your environment, how you think and feel about it and how you appreciate it. With exercise, you can also think more clearly, react more quickly and accomplish tasks more efficiently. Finally, exercise enables you to manifest fully the power of good nutrition in your health.

How it Works

There are a few different kinds of exercises, and each one affects your body and mind differently. The aerobic ones—like long-distance running, swimming, cycling, cross-country skiing, climbing stairs and rowing—help you by maximizing your cardiac output. With exercise, you use up more oxygen and force your heart to pump a higher volume of blood per minute to meet the fuel demands placed upon it by the various tissues. Aerobic activities such as the above therefore help strengthen your heart muscles. Aerobic exercise has many benefits:

1. Because the food gets completely burned into carbon dioxide and water, there is less buildup of toxic substances in the cells. This type of exercise uses the Krebs cycle almost exclusively. The Krebs cycle takes place in the mitochondria of the cells. During this type of exercise, you use up greater amounts of calories than you would in other forms of exercise (see below). Since aerobics enables you to burn fat at a higher rate, it can help you minimize the incidence of heart-related diseases. By increasing your HDL (the good cholesterol), aerobic exercises can protect you against heart attack and atherosclerosis (fat deposits in the arterial walls). For those who want to lose weight, aerobic exercise is indeed very effective. The key is doing it regularly and in conjunction with other weight-reduction methods.

2. Aerobic exercise is perhaps the best for making you feel good and especially euphoric afterwards. During exercise a variety of brain chemicals called endorphins and norepinephrine are produced. It is these chemicals that give you the heightened sense of wellbeing, keenness of mind and euphoria. As a neurotransmitter, epinephrine also enhances your memory and learning ability. When you are mentally sharp, you can accomplish a lot more in life[5]. That is what good, vigorous, regular exercise will do for you.

---

5   In an experiment to show the benefit of exercise to human health, three groups of people were studied. Over a four-month period, one group did aerobics, another did strength exercises like weight lifting and the third (the control group) did nothing. It was found that all those who exercised had an improved reaction time, higher recall rate and improved analytical and reasoning abilities than those who did not exercise. Furthermore, the aerobics group performed even better than those who did strength exercises.' Incidentally, in a similar experiment, children who exercised performed better academically and in other tests that measured their mental and physical abilities.

3. Because exercise in general, and aerobics in particular, pumps more blood through your circulatory system, more oxygen and nutrients are being delivered to the various tissues of your body. It's these nutrients and oxygen that enhance your looks and mental acuity. Notice how those who exercise regularly have something special about the way they look and relate to the world around them. Their skin may be clearer, smoother and more attractive than that of those who don't exercise regularly. These people also seem to be happier and have a higher energy level than their counterparts. As you can deduce from the above information, exercise indeed revitalizes and enhance the quality of your life. Since aerobic fitness enables you to burn more fat, it can also minimize the chance from death related to fat.

4. In another way, exercise rejuvenates your body by neutralizing free radicals—those molecular sharks that annihilate your body tissues at a cellular level. It's thought that since oxygen is used up in greater quantities when you exercise, it must also help neutralize the radicals that form during metabolism. This seems contradictory since we discussed in Appendix A that the most deadly of the radicals (singlet oxygen and peroxides) are formed from oxygen.

When the body is at rest, more of such radicals are formed than neutralized. With exercise, the numbers that are formed are equal to those that are neutralized. Since the oxygen molecule is a rich electron source, those generated from other sources get squelched by the oxygen molecules that bathe the tissue cells.

5. Finally, exercise can induce the release of an important substance known as growth hormone (GH). GH is your body's natural anabolic steroid that helps build muscle mass and strength. Unfortunately, like many other important substances that stop or slow down with age, the production of GH (by the pituitary gland in the brain) wanes after age 30. In those over 30, however, the amino acids arginine and ornithine with vitamin B5 and choline cofactors were shown to increase the production and release of GH.

Strength exercise like weight lifting, sprinting, short putting and discuss throwing, on the other hand, work by helping you build strengthen and tone certain muscles. Although not as vigorously, the heart and lungs also work hard at this type of exercise to bring food and oxygen to meet the energy demands of those specific muscles.

This type of exercise tends to depend less on the Krebs cycle for extraction of energy from foods. Thus such exercises are called anaerobic (without oxygen) exercise. The problem with this form of energy utilization is that food products are not completely burned, and as a result, lactic acid and other chemicals often collect in the muscle tissues. That is why weight lifters and sprinters commonly experience fatigue and cramps in their muscles when they engage in fast and highly intense exercise. . If you want to lose weight or be in good shape, aerobic exercise is your best choice. Anaerobic are good for building strength and for increasing bone and muscle mass.

Another form of exercise that does not affect muscle endurance or the cardio-vascular system is isometric. This type of exercise strives to strengthen or firm muscles by pushing or pulling on a fixed object like a door frame or parallel bars.

Isotonic is a similar form of exercise in which the body works against gravity (i.e., push-ups or free weights). Calisthenics and weight training are examples of isotonic exercise, and they can help you build endurance, muscle strength and muscle mass.

Although they began in Far Eastern countries, where the people practiced them as a way of purifying their minds and bodies through a series of mental and physi-cal exercises, yoga and tai chi have found popularity in the West in the recent past. In these exercises, individuals attempt to attain maximum flexibility and coordina-tion by stretching and breathing properly while simultaneously inducing the mind to free itself from unhealthy thoughts and desires. These exercises are unique in that they deal with the spiritual component of the body. To have a whole and totally integrated body and mind, it's important we work on our spiritual or subconscious mind. In most cases, our subconscious is more powerful in controlling our lives and destiny than any amount of muscles we are able to amass.

To build stamina and endurance and improve your cardiovascular efficiency, you need to do aerobics at least three times a week. Because this type of exercise strengthens the capillaries and encourages the formation of new ones, many of the remote tissues (like skin and scalp) will have more nutrients and oxygen delivered to them. As you must know, this is very important for the appearance of your skin and hair. This type of exercise can also increase the number and size of the mitochondria, the cells energy factories, which enables you to use more oxygen and burn more fuel.

When your heart is fit and strong and it pumps more blood (reportedly 25% and 50% per minute more blood while at rest and during exercise, respectively) and beats less frequently—60 to 70 times per minute as opposed to 80 to a 100 times per minute when you're unfit. Besides making you feel good afterwards by relieving stress and depression, aerobics also minimizes the incidence of cardiovascular diseases such as stroke and heart attack.

To build strength and increase muscle mass, do weight lifting, sprinting and a number of other similar exercises that develop and tone the specific muscle tissues. These exercises will enable you to lift, carry a load and push or pull on an object with power and strength. Simply speaking, these are your power exercises.

On the other hand, to improve flexibility and coordination, do isometric exercise, like gymnastics and calisthenics. These improve your joints' and body's ability to do a whole range of motions—bending, stretching, rotating, etc. These exercises enhance the mechanical efficiency of the body. Unexercised muscles and joints become cranky and stiff—particularly as you get older. Thus, to maintain your youthful attributes and delay the process of aging, do these exercises regularly.

Finally, to achieve a fully integrated mind and body, include yoga, tai chi, meditation, visualization in your daily routine. These exercises will enable you to reach deep within yourself and release mental and spiritual toxins. No matter what you are able to do for your physical self (through various exercises discussed above), you're not completely fit unless you also do the same thing for your mental/spiritual self.

Visualization is perhaps one of the most powerful techniques in achieving almost anything you want, including good health, power and strength, as well as in maintaining your youthful attributes.

In fact, true freedom (whatever that means to you) comes through the spiritual/ mental components of your "self". The relief or freedom you experience after intense workout lasts only through the duration of endorphins and epinephrine that your body produces during these physical exertions—and that is not very long. When you combine the mechanical/physical aspects of body fitness with your spiritual self, you enjoy and appreciate life, and you will look and feel your best.

Nutrition and Exercise

Exercise without a good nutrition program is like driving your car with very of little oil and fuel in it. You may be able to drive it for a little while, but you're not going to get very far. Once all the oil or fuel is used up, the car will come to a grinding halt. This analogy is a good departure point for discussing your nutrition requirements while you pursue your exercise and fitness regimen. Let's follow the analogy a little further.

For your car to run properly, it needs fuel, oil and water. For fuel, you have regular, unleaded and supreme (a high-octane fuel). For oil you can get different grades: 40, 30, 10-40. Similarly, you can also use different water: tap, water (which is bad because the minerals in the water can corrode the water tank and engine overtime) or demineralized or distilled water (which is the best because it has no contamination and does little damage to your car.)

Your body has identical requirements. It needs fuel (food), oil (vitamins and minerals) and water. Like your car, although it can run on regular (proteins) unleaded (fats), its fuel of choice is supreme (carbohydrates—your body's high octane fuel). Strictly as an energy source, proteins are not a good option. Just as regular gas releases lead and other pollutants into the atmosphere, protein burning can release ammonia[6] and other toxins. Ammonia can be very deadly if allowed to build up to a significant level. Fortunately, your body has a built-in safer mechanism by which it can quickly convert this dangerous substance into harmless urea and uric acid. These and other by-products are just as quickly filtered through your kidneys.

The other problem with excessive protein intake is the associated excessive loss of much water. This happens as the body naturally tries to purge itself of the protein-induced pollutants. Incidentally, this problem also burdens your kidneys with extra work—often a prelude to kidney-related diseases that may come later in life. So, when you plan to exercise, avoid eating protein-rich foods beforehand.

6   The form that could temporarily build up is really not ammonia the gas but rather the water-soluble version (ammonium). It is this that the body quickly converts into uric acid. Bear in mind also not all the amino acids from protein can be used as an energy source.

Fats would seem an ideal fuel source for individuals who exercise and do body training—because each molecule of fat has more than twice as much energy stored in it as a similar protein or carbohydrate molecule. (Each gram of fat contains 9 calories, while each gram of protein or carbohydrate contains only 4 calories.) Unfortunately, not only are fats metabolized differently in the body, but also they are very cumbersome substances that have many bad health consequences[7].

Your best fuel supply is carbohydrates. These food groups are the cleanest (highest octane) and most readily available fuel. When athletes like sprinters, gymnasts or weight lifters or when you (in a fight-or-flight situation) need a burst of energy, you depend entirely on glucose—the smallest carbohydrate molecule, derived from foods like rice, pasta and potatoes and other food sources during digestion. This conversion is almost exclusively anaerobic (requiring no oxygen), and it happens in a flash.

The problem with the anaerobic process is that glucose is not completely oxidized, which leads to potential buildup of lactic acid. These acids cause muscle cramps and fatigue when you engage in long and arduous weight lifting or repetitive sprints. They also waste energy because only 5% of the potential energy is extracted from food in this process.

This energy is transferred to ATP (adenosine triphosphate), which serves as a temporary storage medium. Remember, though, that this is very temporary indeed. A sprinter's body, for instance, extracts energy from glucose, transfers it into ATP and uses this same ATP as his source of energy—all of which is done while he is still in motion.

The aerobic (oxygen-dependent) process, on the other hand, involves several steps and takes a little longer, comparatively speaking. This process uses the Krebs cycle solely and is the one in which 95% of the energy is extracted from each glucose molecule. In this reaction, all food molecules are completely oxidized into carbon dioxide and water. Long-distance runners, swimmers and cyclists who need a steady source of energy use the aerobic process almost exclusively.

The other benefit of the aerobic process is that your cells can burn other foods besides carbohydrates. Fats and proteins are equally "combustible" fuels that can be added to the furnace of the Krebs cycle. In endurance exercises like long-distance running, swimming and cycling, however, what becomes a limiting factor is the availability of enough oxygen.

---

7   Since it's not water soluble, it does not get around the body very easily. It needs carrier mediums like HDLs (high density lipoproteins). So, eating large quantities of fat to get your concentrated energy can be a dangerous affair. Some of the fats are free radical generators, others clog the blood vessels leading to cardiovascular diseases.

Just as it takes a strong hand to fan and make a big fire for cooking or heating, it takes a strong heart that can beat steadily and pump large quantities of oxygen-carrying blood per stroke to the furnaces of the mitochondria. Your cardiovascular system has to be free of artery-clogging fats, not only to carry oxygen and nutrients but also to remove the "soot" (carbon dioxide and other waste matter) from the cells.

As you can see from the foregoing discussion, you need aerobic exercises not only to build stamina and endurance but also to lose weight and feel emotionally and physically good. As to shedding extra pounds, the problem most people have is how not to regain it once they lose it.

Traditionally, many weight-loss programs used the Krebs cycle theory to help people lose weight. Since carbohydrates are one of the three competing fuels in the aerobic reactions, it was believed that if you restricted your intake of pasta, rice and other starchy foods, your body would rely on its own fat for energy. By this method, it was thought that over a period of time you could literally melt your fat away.

Although those who endured the agony of this approach may have eventually dropped their extra baggage, they also found it difficult to maintain their new weight. The brain, in normal circumstances, is entirely dependent on glucose for its fuel supply. When you restrict your carbohydrates, you put the brain under a terrible stress. That is why most dieters have a tremendous craving for sweets and feel fatigued and exhausted when they are on a calorie-restrictive program.

Unfortunately, what happens 98% of the time is that these people either end up abandoning the program when they can no longer stand the ordeal or, once they have lost all they want and start eating normally once more, regain all their dearly paid for poundage. Often, they may even add more, because their body wants to store as many calories as possible in the event they starve it again. It might also possibly be interpreted as the body's punishment to them for putting it through this ordeal.

The best solution is to combine aerobic exercise with a high-carbohydrate diet. Carbohydrate-rich diets not only keep your mind sharp and full of energy but also will enable you to undertake your exercise regimen without feeling exhausted. Carbohydrate-based diets also encourage the burning of your body fat, as opposed to contributing to storing it. The key is, once you lose all the pounds you want to lose, keep exercising regularly. This will enable you to maintain your new weight and have overall good health.

APPENDIX D
Losing and Managing Your Weight

Causes of Obesity

Nearly 68% of the American population is either obese or overweight. People have taken many different measures to lose or manage their weight, most without much success. One of the common methods is dieting.

Crash or fad diets deprive the body of key nutrients, reduce lean muscle mass and put the body and mind under enormous stress. This type of dieting, ironically, is also the worst way to try to lose or manage your weight. This is because when important vitamins and minerals are scarce (as they are when you reduce your caloric intake), the body's metabolic processes will be depressed. As a result, not only will your body struggle to mobilize body fat to the mitochondrial furnace of the cell, but it will also have difficulty in efficiently processing the food you consume.

This type of weight loss can be psychologically and emotionally devastating to the individual. When the ordeal becomes unbearable, the person often abandons the program and goes on with life as usual. What do you think is the cause of the weight problem in this country?

Think about it. Save for a few exceptions, people don't just become too fat.

Most often they bring it upon themselves. Here are some of the common reasons why people become overweight.

1. Consuming Too Much Fat

If you are a typical American, chances are you obtain over 40% of your calories from fat and fat-based foods. As much as this food substance is your body's secondary source of energy and offers more calories than similar amounts of carbohydrates and proteins combined, it is also one of the most easily stored substances in the body.

While nearly 25% of the calories from carbohydrates or proteins can be used to convert them into body fat, hardly any calories are expended to convert food fats into body fat. In other words, your body has an "open-door" policy with regard to fats. Hence, as long as you consume too many grams of fat and you have a sedentary lifestyle, these fats simply roll in and get stored in your body tissues.

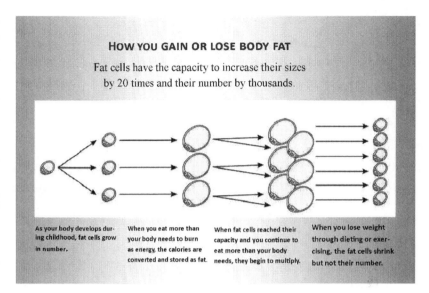

HOW YOU GAIN OR LOSE BODY FAT

Fat cells have the capacity to increase their sizes
by 20 times and their number by thousands.

As your body develops during childhood, fat cells grow in number. · When you eat more than your body needs to burn as energy, the calories are converted and stored as fat. · When fat cells reached their capacity and you continue to eat more than your body needs, they begin to multiply. · When you lose weight through dieting or exercising, the fat cells shrink but not their number.

This is the reason why parents should never let their children to gain weight...Eating junk foods and consuming high-calories soft drinks are the main causes of cardiovascular diseases, cancer, diabetes and a number of other degenerative diseases that afflict us as we get older. Managing our caloric intake and keeping our weight to normal level is very important.

To minimize this problem, experts recommend that you keep your fat calories to below 20% of your total calories.[8]

2.   Consuming Too Many Refined Foods

Processed and refined foods such as sugar and white bread are some of the major culprits regarding the accumulation of excess body fat. Since these foods contain hardly any fiber, they get processed and enter the bloodstream quickly. Because the body's tolerance level for large quantities of sugar is low, this sugar is quickly brought to your body's cells. There, if not used for energy production, it will be converted into and stored as fat.

The consumption of sugar in this country is bad business. Just to show you how bad it has gotten, the per capita consumption of sugar has gone up from 19 pounds per year in 1970 to nearly 70 pounds in 1989.5 This is an amazing 370% increase.

---

8   The American Heart Association and the National Cancer Institute have recommended that we keep our fat calories to below 30% of our total calorie. But for those who have weight problems, experts recommend that fat calories be below 20%.

Where do you think all that sugar ends up? Of course, most of it ends up in your fat cells. As you may know, there are many hidden and visible sugar- based foods. And the problem with an excessive intake of sugar is not limited just to the problem of obesity. You may also have to be concerned about dental cavities, hypertension, hypoglycemia and even adult-onset diabetes.

3.   Sedentary Lifestyle

The average American not only consumes high-calorie foods but also exercises very little. The automobile is omnipresent, and walking even a few hundred yards to a neighborhood store may be viewed as walking a long way. A combination of high calories and no exercise means a higher conversion of those calories into body fat.

As you must know, exercise is one of the great mobilizers of body fat. When your body is at rest, it uses up minimal calories to run the basic bodily functions, such as respiration, digestion and circulation. This so-called basal metabolic rate has been shown to increase with exercise. This means that those who exercise not only burn high calories during the activity but also increase their body's ability to burn fat when at rest.

4.   As You Age Your Metabolism Slows Down

One of the great mysteries of nature is the process of aging. As our bodies age, not only do our skins wrinkle and lose their moisture and our hair thins out, but also the absorption of nutrients from the digestive tract and their metabolism in the cells are compromised. During this time, fat and other calories tend to collect in the tissues at a greater rate than when we were younger. This problem, of course, will cause us to be too fat along with becoming predisposed to degenerative diseases, such as heart diseases, cancer and diabetes.

Things You Can Do About Obesity

From the above discussion, you can see that obesity is largely associated with our consumption of high-calorie foods (fats and too many sweets) as well as from our body's improper utilization of the food we eat (because of a lack of exercise or slowed metabolism). You can also see that the long-term solution to this problem does not come from a crash or fad diet program. It is something we can accomplish by combining well-established weight management techniques with state-of-the-art nutritional ingredients and technology.

1.   Reducing Your Caloric Intake

For a sedentary person, all calories (whether from carbohydrates, fats or proteins) can be fattening when consumed in high amounts. Particularly crucial, however, are those you get from fats. Fat calories, as mentioned above, are treated differently by the body than are other calories. Unlike the calories you get from carbohydrates and proteins, a quarter of which are used up before they turn into body fat, nearly all the fat calories that enter the body go directly into storage. In a country in which over 40% of our calories come from fat, the problem we have with obesity becomes readily apparent.

The best solution to this problem is, obviously, to reduce your daily fat calories to at most 20%, to eliminate or keep to an absolute minimum your daily consumption of sweets and to include regular exercise as part of your weight reduction effort. (You can be generous with your consumption of complex carbohydrates that come from whole foods (teff, brown rice, whole wheat flour and others. These foods can give your body a steady supply of energy.) If you are familiar with the traditional method of weight loss, you can see that the approach described above is revolutionary.

2.   Managing Your Caloric Intake

Along with reducing your consumption of fats and sweets, you may also want to learn how to manage your daily calories. This is to say that although you now have lowered your caloric intake, unless you know how to properly distribute those calories through the day, you may have difficulty in achieving your new weight.

Let's see what this means.

First, remember that any calories that are not used to run your basic bodily functions or your other energy needs are converted into and stored as fat. For example, let's say you have reduced your daily calories from 2,000 to 1,500. Unless you use these new calories wisely, you may not notice a great difference in your weight. How does this happen? Very simply.

Suppose you obtain a significant portion of the 1,500 calories from your evening meal. Since you are less likely to engage in physical activity at night, those calories not utilized by the basal metabolic process will end up in the fatty tissues. Once stored, fat calories are not readily available. (That is why, as discussed below, it takes at least four hours of walking at the rate of 3 miles an hour to lose a pound of body weight.)

Second, when you consume a large portion of your daily calories at night, you will have difficulty containing your hunger during the day and consequently maintaining or reducing your weight. How so? Once calories are stored, the body prefers to keep them for a "rainy day," so to speak. Thus, when the calories from the circulating fluids are depleted as a result of usage or storage, your brain sends hunger signals to the stomach, which you notice when you wake up in the morning or at other times during the day. Often what happens at such times is that you end up eating more at a meal or snacking more frequently on the wrong foods to satisfy the hunger. Neither of these options is going to help you in your weight reduction or maintenance efforts.

To circumvent this problem, you may want to consume a large portion of your 1,500 calories during the day. Since most of us are physically active during the day, we tend to expend a significant proportion of our caloric intake during this time. Thus, at dinner, you may want to have fewer calories but highly nutritious foods. Meals that are rich in protein, vitamins and minerals are preferable.

3.   Using the Four Pillars Drinks and State-of-the-Art Nutritional Ingredients and Supplements

The high mineral and vitamin content in The Four Pillars drinks as well as the fiber and phytonutrient in it should help metabolize fat in your tissues and purge the excesses in foods from the GI tract. Additionally, you may also include nutritional supplements.

In recent past, advances in nutritional science and technology have opened the door to unique and exciting nutritional ingredients and technologies which, if properly used, may enable us to have greater control of our health and well-being. For instance, substances like chromium picolinate and L-carnitine which find in some supplements, are excellent mobilizers of your body's two major fuels: carbohydrates and fats. While chromium picolinate enhances your body's ability to efficiently process and burn sugar and fats, 8 L-carnitine specializes in rounding up fat molecules and dumping them into the mitochondrial furnace. With the availability of these nutrients in your food, less of the sugar and food fat will be converted and stored as body fat. Reportedly, these two substances not only aid you in burning fat but also may help to maintain lean muscle mass.

Equally important in the metabolism of fats and sugars, as mentioned above, is the availability of key vitamins and minerals. In the previous paragraphs, very simplistic terms and analogies were used to describe the mobilization and burning of fats and sugar molecules. What actually goes on in your billions of cells to accomplish the conversion or mobilization of these substances is a very complex process involving millions of chemicals and chemical reactions. For these reactions to come to completion smoothly and efficiently, the availability of sufficient enzymes, minerals and vitamins is crucial.

4.   Exercising Regularly

For losing or controlling weight, as well as for overall good health and a good mental outlook, exercise can make a world of difference in your life. As was briefly mentioned above and is thoroughly discussed in Appendix C, exercise helps the body burn fat during the activity as well as afterwards.

Through a process called lipolysis, exercise encourages the release of fat molecules from their storage sites. This, according to experts, could go on for as long as 24 hours after exercise. Covert Bailey, author of Fit or *Fat,* says that exercise does this by inducing your cells to step up their production of the fat-burning enzymes.

Thus, when you exercise regularly, you will increase the synthesis of these enzymes, which in turn will increase the burning of fat from your body. Aerobic exercises such as running, cross-country skiing, swimming, cycling and climbing stairs are excellent mobilizers of fat deposits. Furthermore, with exercise, you not only build strength and stamina but also increase your lean body mass.

Bear in mind, however, that unless you also include other weight reduction methods, such as taking the fat-mobilizing nutrients discussed above, the amount of poundage you shed through exercise alone over a short period of time can be frustratingly small. For example, to lose just one pound you may need to expend roughly 3,500 calories. This translates into five hours of walking at the rate of 3 miles per hour or four and a half hours of running at 9 miles per hour. Nonetheless, the best way to lose weight is to do it gradually. When you do it slowly, your body is unstressed and the loss can be permanent, as long as you don't overindulge in fattening foods and keep exercising.

What is the best exercise?

For minimizing bodily injuries and for sustaining long-term weight loss, the low-impact types are often considered the best. These are swimming, cycling, walking, climbing stairs, low-impact aerobics, cross country skiing and weight lifting. High-impact exercises—such as downhill skiing, running or jogging, racquetball or basketball—can be stressful to an unconditioned body.

Regardless of the type of low-impact exercise you choose to pursue, bear this in mind: the frequency of the activity is more important than the length of the activity. This, in turn, is more important than the intensity of the activity.

Let me explain this further. Although almost all cells manufacture and store triglycerides (or fat), the ones that synthesize and store them the most are the adipocytes or fat cells (illustrated in Figure D.1). When one is obese, as much as 95% of an adipocyte's volume can be occupied by fat. Hence, when you exercise, the triglycerides are broken down by the lipase enzyme and the free fatty acids diffuse out of the cells and enter the bloodstream which brings them to the working muscles where they are burned as fuel.

As you increase your exercise, more and more blood will flow into the adipose or fat tissues, removing even greater fatty acids. The lipase enzyme is activated by a molecule called cyclic AMP (adenosine monophosphate) which in turn is regulated by the hormones, epinephrine, norepinephrine, glucagon and growth hormones. These hormones are secreted in greater amounts during exercise.

APPENDIX E
The Importance of Good Digestion

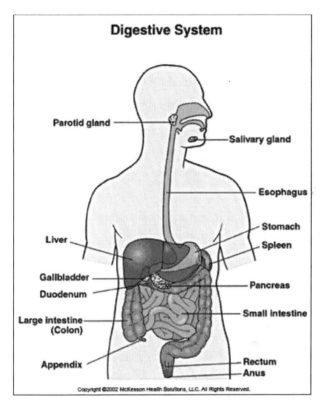

Digestive System

- Parotid gland
- Salivary gland
- Esophagus
- Stomach
- Liver
- Spleen
- Gallbladder
- Duodenum
- Pancreas
- Large intestine (Colon)
- Small intestine
- Appendix
- Rectum
- Anus

Copyright ©2002 McKesson Health Solutions, LLC. All Rights Reserved.

Proper Digestion: The First Step to Good Health

Someone once said that one of the greatest pleasures in life comes from filling and emptying an organ. Regarding this notion, eating is perhaps one of the most pleasurable activities we all engage in every day. It is also a crucial activity because our health and well-being are dependent on the food we eat. Yet most of us have little clue as to what happens to the food we eat once it gets past our lips and into our digestive tract. Like a sunrise or the change of seasons, we take this important, life-giving daily activity of ours for granted. This lack of interest or understanding is perhaps one of the reasons why we have such an unprecedented proportion of food-related degenerative diseases in this country.

As you will see below, much of our day-to-day mental well-being, as well as our long-term health or demise, is dependent not only on the type of foods we put in our bodies but also on how well these foods are digested or processed once they enter our digestive tract.

First, as was mentioned elsewhere in the book, for food to be of any benefit to us, it has to be reduced or broken down to its basic components—proteins to amino acids, fats into glycol and fatty acids and carbohydrates into glucose and other simple sugars. At a microscopic or molecular level, it is these simple molecules that are capable of being transported across the gastrointestinal wall and into the bloodstream. The nutrients are then carried by the blood to the cells where they can be used to fuel, repair and build tissues.

Second, in order for the above nutrients as well as vitamins and minerals to be picked up and transported across the digestive tract, there have to be as few interfering factors as possible. These factors could be substances that trap nutrients and make them unavailable for absorption or those that suppress their transportation across the intestinal wall. Some of these suppressors could be alcohol, cigarettes, coffee and certain medications. Refer to the chapters on vitamins and minerals for specific absorption facilitators and suppressors.

Third, the nutrients that enter the circulatory system should be of the kind that won't upset or disturb the homeostasis ("steady state" conditions) of the body. This means that the foods we ingest should not only have the right balance of nutrients but also be of the kind that won't upset the body's rigidly controlled conditions. It also means that we should eat little or no sugar, sugar-based foods or saturated fats and that we should limit our intake of various foods to the level at which our bodies can process them without too much effort or encumbrance. In this regard, eating small but frequent meals is often considered the best approach.

Here are some of the specific problems that could arise from eating the wrong kind of food. Too much sugar may upset the body's glucose level, which also creates wild mood swings. Saturated fats are bad for the circulatory system. Too much food can strain gastrointestinal walls as well as the various glands that produce the digestive enzymes and juices. In the tissues, excess amounts of these substances must either be converted into fat and stored or be burned or eliminated from the body. If some of these substances are allowed to build up in the circulatory system, they can lead to many unwanted complications.

In order for us to be intimately involved in our health and well-being, we should have a good understanding of the food we eat and how it is processed by the digestive system and the rest of the body. It is amazing how easy it is for us to spend time and money on things that may have no inherent value to our health or long-term survival and do so little for the physical and biochemical self.

Every aspect of our physical, emotional and intellectual well-being is as much a reflection of a properly working digestive system as the variety and diversity of nutrients that enter our bodies. It is with the digestive system that our health's glory or breakdown begins.

The complex and differentiated machinery we call the digestive system functions by reducing long chain and branched food molecules (also known as polymers) into their individual components, so that they are small enough to be absorbed by cells that line the gastrointestinal wall. Let's see how the digestive system breaks down long chain and branched food molecules and readies them for absorption.

The Digestion and Absorption of Nutrients

The first stage of digestion begins in the mouth. Here, the tongue whips the food into a moist mass while the teeth pummel, knead and masticate it. Certain enzymes in the saliva (lipase, amylase and others) begin the initial chemical breakdown of starch and some fat molecules. After the chewing or mastication is complete, the food is turned into a spherical mass known as the bolus, which, with a squeeze and wavelike motion of the throat, is pushed down the esophagus.

The bolus arrives in the stomach. Here a strong acid (called hydrochloric acid) and a medley of enzymes that specialize in snipping and splitting protein, fat and carbohydrate molecules takes action. The stomach, a J-shaped, pot-like organ, is also good at agitating and churning the food as the acid and enzymes untangle and rupture every morsel of food they come in contact with. From here, the food passes down to the small intestine, where, upon its entrance into the upper portion (the duodenum), it is drenched by another medley of digestive juices that come from the gallbladder and the pancreas.

The enzymes trypsin and chymotrypsin function as splitters or reducers of intact or partially digested protein chains. Their job is to reduce them to a size (as amino acids or short peptic chains—as two or three amino acid fragments) that will make it possible for the individual molecules to easily slip across the intestinal wall.

The pancreatic amylase goes about finishing up all the partially digested carbohydrate molecules and maybe even chopping up those that managed to come down untouched by the previous enzymes. Another enzyme, called lipase, goes after fat molecules. The bile from the gallbladder is a handy fluid that helps emulsify or reduce fats to small droplets so that the lipase gets to the individual molecules.

As the food goes down the small intestine, more enzymes are added from the glands that line the wall. These enzymes tend to be those that cleave the last food fragments into individual units: amino acids, glucose and other small sugar molecules. It is these that finally get picked up by a layer of fingerlike projections of the small intestine called villi and microvilli. Because of these tiny microscopic outgrowths, the surface area of the small intestine is increased by over 600 times, which is actually equivalent to the size of a real tennis court. Its length may be only 12 to 15 feet.

It is on the intestinal surface that most of the food gets absorbed. The absorption process can be either by simple diffusion, by active transport (also called facilitated diffusion) or by engulfing. As you will see below, there can be many factors that interfere with this process. It depends largely on the kind of food you eat, the health of the digestive tract and the existence of interfering factors.

The large intestine serves as the place where large quantities of water get removed from waste matter. It also serves as a temporary repository of waste matter.

That, in a nutshell, is how the digestive system works as one whole and integrated unit and serves as a watershed to the cascade of metabolic events that take place later within the trillion of cells in your body. When you think that very little solid food gets past our digestive tract without being broken down by the digestive processes and that life cannot exist without food, you can appreciate the tremendous importance of this living food processor, which we undignified call our "gut." It is the digestive system that gives food meaning and purpose in our lives.

There can also be many disruptive factors that interfere with this process, so let's look at them closely.

Digestion Disrupters

The process of digestion we described above may not be smooth or consistent from day to day or person to person. There are many factors that can disrupt the physiological and chemical processes involved in the digestion of food. Let's start with you. Without being aware of them, there are many things you do just before ingesting food that inhibit the production and secretion of digestive juices as well as interfere with the absorption of nutrients.

One of these could simply be not having sufficient time to sit, relax and enjoy your meal. The process of digestion requires the engaging of all those organs involved in the mobilization and breakdown of food that is placed in the digestive tract. This often entails the activation of key organs along the digestive tract through hormonal stimuli. Sight, smell, taste or even the thought of food can start a whole series of events, which are all concerned in the reception and proper digestion of food that arrives in the digestive system.

Unfortunately, when you eat in a hurry, your focus and energy are not concentrated on your food. This means that not only are all those key digestive organs not activated properly but also the food you consume will be under utilized by your body. The food consumed under such circumstances often stays longer than usual in the digestive tract and causes cramps, distention, constipation or diarrhea.

Similarly, depression, anxiety, overexcitement or stress can cause you to temporarily lose interest in food. Even if you have no physical or emotional disturbances, such simple practices as eating sweets, drinking too many caffeine-based beverages or alcohol or smoking cigarettes and other stimulants can have an equally disruptive effect on your digestive system. They could lead to a whole range of temporary or permanent problems involving the health of the digestive tract, including infections, ulcers, food poisoning and chronic diseases.

Another important concern you may have is what happens to the digestive organs and processes as you age. Unfortunately, like everything else in your body that atrophies with age, the digestive tract and all the organs that contribute to its function reduce their output of digestive juices. This in itself can be a limiting factor in the absorption and utilization of nutrients by the body. Add to this the fact that because most of the food in this country is processed, canned and prematurely harvested, there is a low nutrient content in foods.

Thus, not only do you have many of the disruptive factors mentioned above, but also you are dealing with a situation in which you might not be getting enough nutrients even if you have a healthy lifestyle. Although the health-eroding aspects of all the above factors are not apparent to you now, as the years pass, you may start to feel their impact.

Your Solution

The best thing that you can do to deal with some of the problems is to treat the whole activity of eating like an event, a celebration of something important in your life. Treat it with respect. Enjoy the anticipation as well as the act of consuming your meals. Take your time or slow down when you sit down to eat your meals.

Nothing in life should be more important than your health and well-being. After a meal, relax for 15 to 30 minutes before you engage in any activity. By doing so, you can help your body concentrate its energy in processing the meal. This may enhance the digestion as well as the absorption of nutrients. If you are hungry but don't have time to sit down and have a relaxed meal, have something simple instead, like an apple or water. This option can help kill your hunger and sustain your body until you have time to sit down and enjoy your meal.

You may want to avoid or minimize your intake of the absorption-disruptive foods and drinks mentioned elsewhere in the book before your meals. Although you may have no control over certain infections or chronic digestive disorders, you should have control over such everyday problems as stress, depression, anxiety or overexcitement. Even a chronic condition and infection can be dealt with effectively if you have the right kinds and sufficient amounts of nutrients in your body.

Digestion Disturbances

One of the by-products of digestion is what we often euphemistically refer to as gas. It's largely produced when bacteria in the stomach work on an improperly digested food. This happens, for example, if you eat your food too fast—without thoroughly chewing it and allowing the hydrochloric acid (HCl) and enzymes to break it down in the stomach. This means that before you're ready to eat, think about food. Think of some of the succulent foods you have eaten in the past. These thought processes stimulate the secretions of all the digestive enzymes in the saliva, the stomach lining and the pancreas gland. HCl, the strongest chemical in your stomach, kills bacteria and viruses and helps break down many of the foods. It is also produced in greater quantities when you mentally stimulate the secreting glands along the stomach wall.

A food that is not properly digested can become food for the bacteria in your intestines instead of for your body. The bacteria can start to break down this food and use it, creating gas as a waste product. Often, you may have noticed that when you eat your food in hurry, you end up with cramps and discomfort in your stomach.

This food tends to stay longer in your system, causing pain and constipation. It's believed that one of the causes of colon cancer is when such food putrefies and the bacteria convert it into carcinogenic chemicals. High-protein and lower-fiber foods tend to linger longer and, as a result, putrefy and produce carcinogenic chemicals.

Some foods are more gas generating than others. Most protein foods, especially those rich in sulfur like eggs, cauliflower, beans and broccoli, can be converted into hydrogen-sulfide gas (the most offensive kind) by the intestinal bacteria. Most of the legume family (beans, peas, soybeans, etc.) have two soluble sugars called raffinose and stachyose that are equally gas forming and distending. Most grains, fibers and other plant foods convert into methane gas, which is not as penetrating and jarring to the nostrils.

Fibers can sometimes be a double-edged sword. They have many healthful properties in the digestive tract, but to some people, they can also be a nuisance because the bacteria in their intestines digest them and produce gas. There are some remedies to this problem, however. When you eat fiber-rich foods or supplements for the first time, try to take them in small quantities. The key is not to overwhelm your intestinal bacteria with too much fiber for the first time, in which case they begin to proliferate and start a feeding frenzy and produce large quantities of gas. Just start slowly and build up to the normal serving level.

There are also drugs you can take. The easiest and the safest remedy is activated charcoal, which you can buy from your local drug store or health-food outlet. It comes as a tablet or powder, and it's a powerful absorbent of stomach gases. Just take two to three tablets of this harmless substance with your meal and you should see an improvement.

You may also be one of those people who cannot properly metabolize milk, or rather, the milk sugar (lactose). The milk-processing enzyme, lactase, may be lacking in your digestive system, leaving the milk to be processed by the bacteria into gas. In this case, the easiest remedy is, of course, to avoid milk and milk products.

In summary, just remember that your overall health and well-being and even longevity are dependent on the nutrients that are processed and provided by your gastrointestinal tract. Without the proper functioning of this system, there is no there is no beautiful hair, skin or healthy and properly working body and mind.

APPENDIX F
Enzymes: The Keys of Life

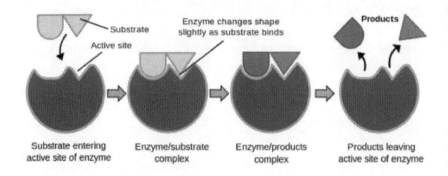

| Substrate entering active site of enzyme | Enzyme/substrate complex | Enzyme/products complex | Products leaving active site of enzyme |

Enzymes

We have now come to what is perhaps the most important and fundamental component of good health, wellness and longevity: enzymes. We have referred to Enzymes quite often in this book. Let's now take a close look at these wonders of nature a little closely.

Unlike vitamins, minerals and herbs, which directly or indirectly affect the function of the body, enzymes (as discussed in Appendix E), control the very fundamental processes or operations of the body. These range from the breakdown of foods in the digestive tract to their assembly or synthesis in the tissues and organs to their conversion into energy. In short, enzymes are the key that unlocks the essence of food in the body to give it strength, wellness, and vitality. This means that without enzymes, life would not exist and food would have no meaning or purpose.

What exactly are enzymes, and where are they made, you may ask. Enzymes are a special group of protein molecules that somehow behave as if they had a soul and a life of their own. They do what they do (break down food, synthesize or assemble food molecules, etc.) without instruction (at least as far as we know) from anywhere.

They are the architects and the laborers as well as the housekeepers of our body. Everything that we are and do is controlled or facilitated by enzymes. This can range from thinking to blinking our eyes to engaging in physical tasks as well as to building and repairing tissues.

The body contains two major classes of enzymes: digestive enzymes and metabolic enzymes. The digestive enzymes are synthesized in the pancreas and in the cell along the gastrointestinal tract as well as in other cells in the body. These enzymes are responsible for the breakdown or digestion of food. The metabolic enzymes are produced by every cell in the body and are involved in the conversion of food into energy or in using food to build and repair tissues.

Enzymes also can get involved in processing or converting toxins and pollutants into harmless substances. This is their scavenging function. Considering that many of us live in a polluted environment and consume food and water that may have been exposed to dubious chemicals, this housekeeping function of enzymes can be very important indeed.

Outside the body is a third class of enzymes, called food enzymes. As their name implies, these enzymes are responsible for all the activities that take place in plants, from germinating a seed to its growing and maturing into a plant to its blossoming and bearing fruit. Just as an organism decomposes after death with the help of its own enzymes, the enzymes in plants are responsible for making plants biodegradable. Most of the food enzymes are similar to the enzymes found in our bodies.

The Importance of Enzyme Supplements for Our Health

Before we discuss the significance of enzyme supplements to our health and well-being, let's talk about the specific functions of the different digestive enzymes found in our bodies. As you can see in the discussion on digestion in previous section, there are specific enzymes for the different classes of foods we consume every day. Hence, protease specializes in processing proteins; lipase, in breaking down fats; and amylase, lactase, cellulase in snipping and splitting starch, lactose and cellulose molecules, respectively. (Starch, lactose and cellulose are all carbohydrates.)

It can be said that nearly every single food molecule (or, for that matter, every chemical reaction) has its own specific enzyme that helps catalyze the conversion or breakdown of that food (or chemical substance).

It may be self-evident that without sufficient quantities of all the above enzymes, foods cannot be properly processed, and consequently our health and wellness could suffer. Does this mean that we need to be concerned about our supply of enzymes? Can there be a shortage or depletion of our enzyme supply? If so, could we benefit from an enzyme supplement? Let's answer each of these questions separately.

Our body's production of enzymes will depend on our age, the type of food we have been consuming throughout life and the stress and pollution levels we have subjected our bodies to.

Like everything else that happens to tissues and organs as we get older, our bodies' ability to secrete sufficient quantities of enzymes declines. For instance, in one study, the concentration of the enzyme amylase in the saliva of young adults was found to be 30 times stronger than in individuals over 69 years old. In another experiment, the concentration and strength of the same enzyme taken from the pancreas of a group of older men were found to be many times weaker than that taken from the pancreas of younger men.

Besides the normal aging process, extended consumption of processed, cooked and irradiated foods can deplete the body's reserve of both metabolic and digestive enzymes. As mentioned above, when consuming foods that have been processed and altered, (i.e., foods whose enzymes have been destroyed), the body has to produce a large quantity of its own to digest and utilize such food. Interestingly, like muscles that increase in mass from the challenge of physical exertion, glands and organs responsible for the secretion of digestive juices and enzymes enlarge when repeatedly burdened with a large quantity of processed and cooked foods. This fact has been demonstrated by comparing the pancreas of wild mice (mice that feed on raw food) with the pancreas of laboratory mice that were fed processed and cooked food.

Likewise, when our body is exposed to pollution or extraneous chemicals such as pesticides and food additives (preservatives, coloring and flavoring agents), it will use (and therefore waste) a large quantity of its own enzymes. This happens because, our liver, kidneys and other organs and tissues use enzymes to process or turn some of these chemicals (as well as viruses) into harmless substances. As these organs and tissues are stressed or burdened with the production of a large quantity of enzymes, they naturally enlarge to increase production and meet the demand placed upon them.

When we eat whole, uncooked foods, the enzymes that are naturally found in them can help break down those foods in the digestive tract. Cooking or microwaving foods destroys enzymes. This habitual practice will lead to our being dependent on our own enzymes to process the food and consequently may lead to the depletion of our bodies' reserve of enzymes. The long-term consequence of this reckless usage of our bodies' labor force can be a decline in the bodies' function, a greater susceptibility to degenerative diseases and in general a higher compromise of our health and wellness.

The above piece of information is one reason why the Four Pillars drinks—all prepared from raw fruits, vegetables and herbs—become healthy alternatives to similar processed and cooked foods people consume often.

What is the solution to the above problem? The first solution to this challenge is to consume whole and uncooked foods as much as possible (like the Four Pillars drinks). Because the enzymes that are naturally found in uncooked foods can help digest such foods, the body will produce fewer of its own enzymes in the presence of these foods. In other words, to quote Dr. Edward Howell, author of Enzyme Nutrition, "If we depend solely upon the enzymes we inherit, they will be used just like inherited money that is not supplemented with a steady income." The uncooked, whole food may serve as a good source of that supplemental, steady supply of enzyme income.

The second solution, if for some reason you're not making your Four Pillars drink as often or don't bother making it, is to use prepackaged enzyme supplements. Because processed, cooked and chemically adulterated foods are omnipresent, augmenting your diet with quality enzyme supplement may be a good alternative. That way you may conserve your body's reserve of enzymes as well as help you process your food efficiently.

Use a supplement that has multiple enzymes, or enzymes that can help you process protein, carbohydrates and fat. Hence, for example, while protease, peptidase, help you to digest proteins, amylase, invertase, glucoamylase and lactase can help your body break down carbohydrates. Similarly, a lipase enzyme can help you process fat. As we said above, enzymes can very specific in their function. Thus, the above different protein and carbohydrate enzymes can help you digest some of the most common carbohydrates and proteins found in ordinary foods, when taken as part of a supplement.

Acknowledgement

My wife, Rosario, has been my ardent fan and supporter of my work. She has allowed me the quiet and secluded space I needed to write this book, for which I'm appreciative and thankful.

I extend my many thanks to Philip Howe for his artistic wizardry with this and my other books and for his patience and understanding of my need to make the illustrations as vivid and authentic as possible. I thank Greg Brown for his professional work in the formatting and designing of the book's interior. I thank my nephew, Tadesse Alemayehu Ambaw who provided me the details for some of the beverage preparations. Time had clouded my memories.

Glossary

A

Abol The first coffee in the three rounds of coffee brewing and serving

amli Shiro wot (see below) made from plain pea or chickpea flour, garlic and salt, name coined by the author

alicha Spiced but mild stew usually made from vegetables or legumes but without berbere

areqey Homemade whiskey

atela The residue left after tella is filtered

awaze Red pepper paste made from several spices (ginger, nutmeg, cloves, onions, thyme, cinnamon, garlic, and red chili peppers which have been toasted and formed into a paste; adds heat to meat, seafood, and bread

azifa A dish made from lentils and other ingredients

ayib Cheese harvested from heated butter milk, used as a side dish or added to other foods

B

berbere The base ingredient to many of the Ethiopian dishes made of toasted, dried red chili and a couple dozen spices

bereka The third coffee in the three rounds of coffee brewing and serving

bikil Malt, germinated grain

birchiko A glass drinking cup

birz honey Diluted in water

breent The residue left after areqey distillation

buticha A sauce made from chickpea flour, onions, garlic, ginger jalapeno pepper and oil

D

dagim In areqey- (see above) making, the second and most potent distillate made from combining and distilling the first distillates.

dagussa Millet

difdif The final brewed mixture in tella (home-made beer) preparation

duba Pumpkin

F

Ferenge A white person

finjal Small Coffee drinking cup

G

gembo A tall-necked clay jar

gesho an Ethiopian plant (equivalent to hops) used in tella- (home-made beer-) and tej- (honey wine-) making. It gives these beverages slightly tangy or bitter flavor.

grawa An Ethiopian bush used to sanitize the beer-making vessels

I

injera Soft, stretchy, crepe-like flat bread, made of sourdough starter and teff and baked over clay griddle

ingudai Mushroom

K

kerari The first distillate or extract in areqey (Ethiopian home-made vodka) making

kita Fat flat bread

kitfo Finely chopped beef, seasoned with niter kibbeh (spiced clarified butter) and mitmita

kodda Aluminum flask

kurtet Cutting sensations in the stomach and intestines

kurtmat Painful sensation in the joints and muscles, often experienced by people.

M

madd-bet Kitchen house (literally translated)

mitad Baking pan

miser Lentils

miser wot Lentils stew.

mitmita Very hot chili powder with spices, made from crushed bird's eye chili, cardamom, and salt.

N

netch White.

niter kibbeh Clarified butter made from fenugreek seeds, cumin, kewrerima, chopped onions, ginger, chopped garlic, ground turmeric, cardamom seeds and sacred basil.

S

sa'bia The second distillate or extract in areqey (Ethiopian home-made vodka) making

siljo An aged dip made from either barely or fava beans flour and a mixture of fenugreek, sunflower water, ginger, garlic, mustard powder, fresh rue leaves, salt and water

sambusa Triangular, deep-fried pastry, stuffed with beef, chicken, or vegetables.

T

teff Tiny but hardy, gluten-free grain native to Ethiopia. It is the main flour used to make injera

tej Ethiopian honey wine, brewed from raw honey and hops.

tella Homemade Ethiopian beer often brewed from barley and hops.

tibs Cubed beef, lamb or chicken sauteed with spices.

tikur or tikoor Black

tinjit Used to fumigate beer-preparation container both to sanitize it and impart flavor to the beverage

tona The second coffee in the three rounds of coffee brewing and serving

Y

ye'abesha gomen Chopped collard greens cooked with minced onions, garlic, ground cardamom, fenugreek, and black cumin

W

weyra a type of tree (similar to the olive tree) used to fumigate a tella preparation jug, both to sanitize the container and impart flavor to the beer

weyn tej Wine made from grapes

wonfeet A type of basket with woven mesh at the bottom used for sieving

wot Ethiopia's spiced stew, made with vegetables, fish, chicken, lamb, or beef.

wugat Sharp pain in the chest or abdomen

For the Appendices

A

acid A substance that produces hydrogen ions (H+'s) when in solution.

aerobic metabolism The oxygen-dependent, final breakdown of food molecules occurring in the mitochondria to release energy, carbon dioxide, water and heat.

alpha-tocopherol The most biologically active and widely distributed natural form of vitamin E.

amino acid A group of nitrogen containing compounds that serve as building block for protein molecules.

anaerobic metabolism The breakdown of glucose molecules without oxygen which occurs in the cytoplasm (of the cell). Through this process, only 5% of the energy is extracted from glucose; the other 95% is extracted when the partially processed glucose molecules enter the Krebs cycle in the mitochondria. Anaerobic metabolism takes place usually during intense short-duration physical exertion such as sprinting, weight lifting and downhill skiing.

antioxidants Electron-rich chemicals or nutrients used to minimize or eliminate oxidation. A number of nonfood-and food-based chemicals are used for this purpose. For example, vitamins A, C and E and the amino acids cysteine, methionine and taurine are well-documented antioxidants used to neutralize the damaging effect of free radicals. Nonfood chemicals, such as butylated hydroxytoluene (BHT) and butylated hydroxyanisole (BHA), ate common anti-oxidants added to food to slow down the aging or spoiling of foods.

ascorbic acid An alternate name for vitamin C. Vitamin C helps the absorption of iron and is an excellent antioxidant. It is also important for the health, growth and normal functioning of teeth, bones, gums and muscles.

B

basal metabolic rate The metabolic rate of the body at rest.

basal metabolism The minimum amount of energy needed by the body to maintain vital processes, i.e., circulation, respiration and digestion.

beta-carotene Precursor of vitamin A found mostly in yellow and orange vegetables. Beta carotene is an excellent antioxidant, particularly against the singlet oxygen free radicals. This water-soluble vitamin also has many other healthful properties.

beta cells The cells in the pancreas that manufacture insulin.

bile A pigmented fluid secreted by the liver and stored in the gallbladder that helps with the digestion of fats upon entry into the duodenum (upper portion of the small intestine). Bile can be yellow, green or brown, depending on the relative concentration of salts, acids, cholesterol, lecithin (a fat-emulsifying agent) and a number of other colored compounds. When these pigmented chemicals mix with digestion by-products in the intestine, they give feces its brown color.

bilirubin A bile component that is a breakdown of hemoglobin of the red blood cells. Bilirubin is responsible for the brown appearance of stool.

bioavailability The amount of nutrient (or chemical) that is available to the body in relation to the total ingested amount.

bioflavonoids A group of related compounds that act as special helpers of Vitamin C. These pigmented substances team up with Vitamin C to help us maintain a healthy immune system as well as properly working muscular and other tissues.

Bromelain A protein-digesting enzyme obtained from pineapple.

C

caffeine A chemical substance obtained from coffee, tea and chocolate that serves as a stimulant to the nervous system.

calcium A major component of bones and teeth is also involved in muscle contraction, nerve impulse transmission and blood clotting.

calcium ascorbate A less acidic form of vitamin C that is also a highly absorbable form of calcium.

calorie A measurement of energy that is equivalent to the amount of heat required to raise the temperature of one gram of water by one degree Celsius. In nutrition, "calorie" is used to indicate the energy value of foods. One calorie (also referred to as a kilocalorie) is equal to 1,000 calories.

carbohydrates One of the three classes of food substances that provide the body with energy. There are !generally three classes of carbohydrates: monosaccharides (i. e., glucose, galactose and fructose), disaccharides (i. e., table sugar, lactose and honey) and 'polysaccharide (heat, corn, potatoes, etc.). Chemically, carbohydrates are made up of carbon, hydrogen and oxygen atoms.

carcinogen A substance that causes cancer in living tissues.

carotene A fat-soluble plant pigment some of which can be converted into vitamin A in the body.

catabolism The breakdown of nutrients (carbohydrates, proteins and fats) or body tissues to provide energy and other necessary metabolic functions. (See also anabolism and metabolism) catalyst A substance that speeds up the rate of chemical reaction without being consumed itself.

cell The basic building block of body tissues.

cell membrane The outer covering of a cell.

ceruloplasmins The combination of copper with plasma protein believed to protect the red blood cells from free radicals.

cholesterol A fat-like substance found in the blood and in most animal tissues. Cholesterol is one of the important constituents of cell membranes and it serves as precursor to many hormones and bile salts. Cholesterol is not found in plants.

coenzyme A non-protein organic substance that assists enzymes in doing their job well. Coenzymes often contain B vitamins in their molecular structures.

cofactor Another non-protein substance that is involved during an enzyme-catalyzed reaction. Certain minerals often function as cofactors.

constipation An abnormally difficult or infrequent passage of stool. An increased consumption of dietary fiber, the use of laxatives or an enema can often be an effective solution to constipation.

D

diabetes A degenerative disease characterized by abnormally high blood sugar as a result of a malfunctioning pancreas and thus an insufficient production of insulin.

diet The variety of foods that a person consumes habitually.

Dietary fiber The indigestible part of food (i.e., of fruits, vegetables and carbohydrates) that is not processed and absorbed for energy or other bodily purposes. Dietary fiber is divided into four groups: cellulose, hemicellulose, legnins and pectins. Dietary fiber is believed to be important in minimizing the incidence of colon cancer, diverticulosis, diabetes, obesity, constipation and a number of intestinal disorders.

digestion The breakdown of foods in the digestive tract into their simpler components for absorption and processing by the body.

digestive tract All the organs (mouth, esophagus, stomach, small intestine and colon) involved in the digestion and absorption of food.

DL-alpha tocopherol Synthetic vitamin E. This forms of vitamin is less biologically active than d-alpha tocopherol.

DNA The genetic material found in the cells of nearly all living things, which controls the transmission of heredity or hereditary traits. DNA stands for deoxyribonucleic acid.

duodenum The first 12-inch portion of the small intestine that receives bile and pancreatic juice from the gallbladder and pancreas, respectively. edema The accumulation of excess water in body tissues. This problem is often observed in protein deficiency conditions.

E

enzyme A biological substance (usually a protein) that initiates and speeds up a biochemical reaction.

essential amino acids A group of (8 to 9) amino acids that are not synthesized by the body and that must be obtained from dietary sources.

extract A concentrated form of a natural product obtained by treating an herbal with a solvent and then completely or partially removing the solvent. In this manner a variety of extracts called liquid extracts, solid extracts, powder extracts, tinctures and native extracts can be obtained.

F

fats One of the three classes of nutrients that provide your body with energy. Fats can supply 9 calories per gram. There are three different types of fats:saturated (found mostly in animal products), monounsaturated and polyunsaturated (obtained from plants).

fat-soluble vitamin A vitamin molecule that is transported by fats in the body. Vitamins A, E, D and K are the only known fat-soluble vitamins.

fatty acid An organic molecule consisting of a chain of hydrogen-containing carbon atoms with a few oxygen atoms.

fiber See dietary fiber

flavonoid A term used to refer to a group of flavon-containing compounds or plant pigments such as anthocyanins, anthoxanthins, bioflavonols, flavonols, flavons and apeginens. It is now know that the flavonoids have a tremendous effect on the human body.

free radical A very unstable and highly reactive molecular fragment, which is known to cause a number of problems in the body, including aging.

G

gastric juice The colorless secretions of the gastric glands of the stomach. The major constituents of gastric juices are hydrochloric acid (which makes it very acidic, pH 2), pepsin, mucin and renin (in infants). The gastric juice is a very powerful neutralizer and deactivator of bacteria, viruses and a number of unwanted substances. It also is important for the absorption of minerals and vitamin B12.

glucose The most common monosaccharide found in fruits, sugars and starch. Glucose (sometimes called dextrose) is an important source of energy for the body and a primary source of fuel for the brain. In the blood, the optimal level of glucose is 5 milli-mole/liter. In a healthy person, the constancy of glucose is monitored by two hormones: insulin and glucagon. When there is an abnormally high level of glucose, insulin helps bring it down to normal by facilitating the cells' uptake of the sugar. Glucagon does the opposite: it helps break down glycogen (the body's stored sugar) when there is an abnormally low level of glucose in the blood.

glutathione peroxidase A powerful free-radical quenching enzyme produced in the body from the sulfur-containing amino acid glutamine and the mineral selenium.

glycogen Often referred to as animal starch, glycogen is a polysaccharide made by the body from excess glucose. The conversion of glucose into glycogen and the storing of this energy source are nature's ways of dealing with excesses or shortages.

H

HDL (high-density lipoprotein) cholesterol A tightly "packaged" cholesterol that can easily and efficiently move through the blood vessels.

I

immunity The body's ability to fend off infections due to the production of specialized cells such as the white blood cells and antibodies.

insulin A sugar-metabolizing hormone that is secreted by the pancreas gland.

intestinal flora Microorganisms found in the intestinal tract that are believed to have many useful functions, including the production of vitamin K, the blood-clotting nutrient.

K

Krebs cycle An energy-producing process that occurs in the mitochondria of the cell. It's in the Krebs cycle that the maximum amount of energy is extracted from the food you eat. The other by-products of this process are carbon dioxide, water and heat.

L

lactic acid A by-product of glucose metabolism formed due to inadequate levels of oxygen in the cell. Lactic acid is generally formed during strenuous physical activities such as weight lifting, sprinting and other continuous, repetitive physical exertions.

M

metabolism All the chemical and physical processes that take place within the body to ensure survival and proper development of the body.

minerals All the inorganic nutrients that are used during metabolism, as well as those that serve as structural components.

mitochondria A cellular power plant. In a process called the Krebs cycle, all oxygen-dependent reactions take place in the mitochondria.

monoamine oxidase (MAO) An enzyme that catalyzes the breakdown of mono-amines such as epinephrine, serotonin and norepinephrine. MAO is found in all tissues, but in particularly rich quantities in the liver and the nervous system. Drugs that inhibit the activity of this enzyme are effective in the treatment of depression.

N

nutrient A food substance that is essential for the growth, repair and maintenance of body tissues.

nutrient density The ratio of nutrients to calories obtained from a food source. If a food contains a small amount of calories in relation to its nutrient content, that food is thought to be nutrient dense.

O

obesity The accumulation of excess fat in a person's body. A person is said to be obese if he/she is 20% above the recommended weight for his/her height and build.

oil A fat that is liquid at room temperature.

P

polyunsaturated fatty acids Fatty acids containing two or more double bonds.

protein One of the three classes of foods that are used for structural and functional purposes. Proteins are built from a chain of amino acids. Proteins differ from carbohydrates or fats by the nitrogen atom in their chain.

R

Recommended Dietary Allowance (RDA) Officially recommended amounts of various nutrients.

S

saturated fat A fat molecule containing the maximum number of hydrogen atoms in its fatty acid portionssedative A substance the calms or tranquilizes the body.

stimulant An agent that temporarily hyperactivates a tissue or an organ.

T

tea An infusion made by adding hot water to an herb for use as medicine or as a beverage. Herbal tea is usually made by steeping one teaspoon of the herb in eight ounces of water.

tincture An alcoholic solution of herbal active ingredients prepared by percolation or dilution of their corresponding fluid or native extracts. Although the alcohol amount may vary, the tincture strength is usually 1:10 or 1:5.

tonic A substance that nourishes, restores and strengthens the entire body.

toxic A poisonous substance that can be of a plant or animal origin

U

unsaturated fatty acids A fatty acid containing at least one double bond.

V

vegetarian A person who consumes vegetables and grains exclusively—anything but animal products

vitamin Essential nutrient that must be obtained from food sources for the proper growth and function of the body.

vitamin A palmitate One of the antioxidant vitamins that is also important for growth and the proper functioning of the eyes, healthy skin, hair and the lining of the digestive tract.

W

western diet A diet in Western societies that consists of high fat, low fiber and refined and processed foods.

water-soluble vitamin A vitamin that dissolves in water. All of the eight B vitamins and vitamin C are water soluble.

PART VI
References

Ethiopian spices

Chapter 4
Beso Bela (Sacred Basil)

- http://www.medicinehunter.com/holy-basil
- Singh N, Misra N, Srivastava AK, Dixit KS, Gupta GP. Effect of anti-stress plants on biochemical changes during stress reaction. *Indian Journal of Pharmacology.* 1991;23:137–142
- Evidence-Based Complementary and Alternative Medicine Volume 2012 (2012), Article ID 894509, 7 pages
- *Indian Journal of Experimental Biology,* Vol. 40, July 2002, pp. 765-773
- Sembulingam K, Sembulingam P, Namasivayam A. Effect of Ocimum sanctum Linn on the changes in central cholinergic system induced by acute noise stress.
- *J Ethnopharmacol.* 2005 Jan 15;96(3):477-82.
- Sembulingam K, Sembulingam P, Namasivayam A. Effect of Ocimum sanctum Linn on noise induced changes in plasma corticosterone level. *Indian J Physiol Pharmacol.* 1997 Oct;41(4):429-30.
- Archana R, Namasivayam A. Effect of Ocimum sanctum on noise induced changes in neutrophil functions. *J Ethnopharmacol.* 2000 Nov;73(1-2):81-5.
- Sen P, Maiti PC, Puri S, Ray A, Audulov NA, Valdman AV. Mechanism of antistress activity of Ocimum sanctum Linn, eugenol and Tinospora malabarica in
- experimental animals. Indian J Exp Biol. 1992 Jul;30(7):592-6.

Chapter 5
Dimbilal (Coriander)

- http://www.whfoods.com/genpage.php?tname=foodspice&dbid=70
- Ballal RS, Jacobsen DW, Robinson K. Homocysteine: update on a new risk factor. Cleve Clin J Med 1997 Nov-1997 Dec 31;64(10):543-9. 1997.
- Chithra V, Leelamma S. Hypolipidemic effect of coriander seeds (Coriandrum sativum): mechanism of action. Plant Foods Hum Nutr 1997;51(2):167-72. 1997. PMID:12610.
- Chithra V, Leelamma S. Coriandrum sativum changes the levels of lipid peroxides and activity of antioxidant enzymes in experimental animals. Indian J Biochem Biophys 1999 Feb;36(1):59-61. 1999. PMID:12590.

- Delaquis PJ, Stanich K, Girard B et al. Antimicrobial activity of individual and mixed fractions of dill, cilantro, coriander and eucalyptus essential oils. Int J Food Microbiol. 2002 Mar 25;74(1-2):101-9. 2002.
- Ensminger AH, Esminger M. K. J. e. al. Food for Health: A Nutrition Encyclopedia. Clovis, California: Pegus Press; 1986. 1986. PMID:15210.
- Fortin, Francois, Editorial Director. The Visual Foods Encyclopedia. Macmillan, New York. 1996.
- Gray AM, Flatt PR. Insulin-releasing and insulin-like activity of the traditional anti- diabetic plant Coriandrum sativum (coriander). Br J Nutr 1999 Mar;81(3):203-9. 1999. PMID:12600.
- Grieve M. A Modern Herbal. Dover Publications, New York. 1971.
- Kubo I, Fujita K, Kubo A, Nihei K, Ogura T. Antibacterial Activity of Coriander Volatile Compounds against Salmonella choleraesuis. *J Agric Food Chem.* 2004 Jun 2;52(11):3329-32. 2004. PMID:15161192.
- Wood, Rebecca. The Whole Foods Encyclopedia. New York, NY: Prentice-Hall Press; 1988. 1988. PMID:15220.

Chapter 6
Inslal (Anise)

- Anise. Review of Natural Products. factsandcomparisons4.0 [online]. 2005. Available from Wolters Kluwer Health, Inc. Accessed April 16, 2007.
- Anise (*Pimpinella anisum* L.) from Gernot Katzer's Spice Pages, How to Grow Anise from growingherbs.org.uk
- Philip R. Ashurst (1999). *Food Flavorings*. Springer. p. 33. ISBN 978-0-8342-1621-1.
- J.S. Pruthi: Spices and Condiments, New Delhi: National Book Trust (1976), p. 19.
- J "Anise History". *Our Herb Garden*. Retrieved 3 March 2013.
- Jack S. Blocker, Jr.; David M. Fahey; Ian R. Tyrrell (2003). *Alcohol and Temperance in Modern History: An Global Encyclopedia*. ABC-CLIO. pp. 478–.ISBN 978-1-57607-833-4. Retrieved 28 March 2013.
- John Gerard, *The Herball, or Generall Historie of Plantes*, 1597, p. 880, side 903

Chapter 7
IRD (Turmeric)

- http://www.whfoods.com/genpage.php?tname=foodspice&dbid=78

- Abbey M, Noakes M, Belling GB, Nestel PJ. Partial replacement of saturated fatty acids with almonds or walnuts lowers total plasma cholesterol and low-density-lipoprotein cholesterol. Am J Clin Nutr 1994 May;59(5):995-9. 1994. PMID:16240.

- Aggarwal B. Paper presented at the U.S. Defense Department's 'Era of Hope' Breast Cancer Research Program meeting in Philadelphia, PA, October 5, 2005,. reported in NUTRAingredients.com/Europe "Turmeric slows breast cancer spread in mice.".

- Ahsan H, Parveen N, Khan NU, Hadi SM. Pro-oxidant, anti-oxidant and cleavage activities on DNA of curcumin and its derivatives demethoxycurcumin and bisdemethoxycurcumin. Chem Biol Interact 1999 Jul 1;121(2):161-75. 1999. PMID:7690.

- Arbiser JL, Klauber N, Rohan R, et al. Curcumin is an in vivo inhibitor of angiogenesis. Mol Med 1998 Jun;4(6):376-83. 1998. PMID:7540.

- Asai A, Nakagawa K, Miyazawa T. Antioxidative effects of turmeric, rosemary and capsicum extracts on membrane phospholipid peroxidation and liver lipid metabolism in mice. Biosci Biotechnol Biochem 1999 Dec;63(12):2118-22. 1999. PMID:7550.

- Balasubramanian K. Molecular Orbital Basis for Yellow Curry Spice Curcumin's Prevention of Alzheimer's Disease.*J. Agric. Food Chem.*, 54 (10), 3512 -3520, 2006.

- Calabrese V, Butterfield DA, Stella AM. Nutritional antioxidants and the heme oxygenase pathway of stress tolerance: novel targets for neuroprotection in Alzheimer's disease. *Ital J Biochem.* 2003 Dec;52(4):177-81. 2003.

- Calabrese V, et. al. Paper on curcumin's induction of hemeoxygenase-1. Presented at the annual conference of the American Physiological Society, held April 17-21, 2004, Washington, D.C. 2004.

- Cruz-Correa M, Shoskes DA, Sanchez P, Zhao R, Hylind LM, Wexner SD, Giardiello FM. Combination treatment with curcumin and quercetin of adenomas in familial adenomatous polyposis. i>Clin Gastroenterol Hepatol. 2006 Aug;4(8):1035-8. Epub 2006 Jun 6. 2006. PMID:16757216.

- Deshpande UR, Gadre SG, Raste AS, et al. Protective effect of turmeric (Curcuma longa L.) extract on carbon tetrachloride-induced liver damage in rats. Indian J Exp Biol 1998 Jun;36(6):573-7. 1998. PMID:7740.

- Dorai T, Cao YC, Dorai B, et al. Therapeutic potential of curcumin in human prostate cancer. III. Curcumin inhibits proliferation, induces apoptosis, and inhibits angiogenesis of LNCaP prostate cancer cells in vivo. Prostate 2001 Jun 1;47(4):293-303. 2001. PMID:16280.

- Egan ME, Pearson M, Weiner SA, Rajendran V, Rubin D, Glockner-Pagel J, Canny S, Du K, Lukacs GL, Caplan MJ. Curcumin, a major constituent of turmeric, corrects cystic fibrosis defects. *Science*. 2004 Apr 23;304(5670):600-2. 2004. PMID:15105504.

- Ensminger AH, Esminger M. K. J. e. al. Food for Health: A Nutrition Encyclopedia. Clovis, California: Pegus Press; 1986. 1986. PMID:15210.

Chapter 8
Kewrerima (False Cardamom)

- *Aframomum corrorima* was published in *Spices, Condiments and Medicinal Plants in Ethiopia, Their Taxonomy and Agricultural Significance*. (Agric. Res. Rep. 906 & Belmontia New Series) 12:10. 1981. The specific epithet was taken from its basionym,*Amomum corrorima* A.Braun GRIN (April 9, 2011). "*Aframomum corrorima* information from NPGS/GRIN". *Taxonomy for Plants*. National Germplasm Resources Laboratory, Beltsville, Maryland: USDA, ARS, National Genetic Resources Program. RetrievedJune 19, 2011. Synonyms: (≡) *Amomum corrorima* A.Braun (basionym)

- *Amomum corrorima* A.Braun, the basionym of *Aframomum corrorima* (A.Braun) P.C.M.Jansen, was originally described and published in *Flora* 31:95. 1848 GRIN. "*Amomum corrorima* information from NPGS/GRIN". *Taxonomy for Plants*. National Germplasm Resources Laboratory, Beltsville, Maryland: USDA, ARS, National Genetic Resources Program. Retrieved June 19, 2011.

- Bernard Roussel and François Verdeaux (April 6–10, 2003). "Natural patrimony and local communities in ethiopia: geographical advantages and limitations of a system of indications" (PDF). *29th Annual Spring Symposium of Centre for African Studies*. Archived from the original (PDF) on 2006-11-26. This Zingiberaceae, *Aframomum corrorima*(Braun) Jansen, is gathered in forests, and also grown in gardens. It is a basic spice in Ethiopia, used to flavor coffee and as an ingredient in various widely used condiments (berbere, mitmita, awaze, among others).

- J Jansen, P.C.M. (2002). "Aframomum corrorima (Braun)". Archived from the original on 2008-11-20. P.C.M. Jansen. Record from Protabase. Oyen, L.P.A. & Lemmens, R.H.M.J. (Editors). PROTA (Plant Resources of Tropical Africa / Ressources végétales de l'Afrique tropicale), Wageningen, the Netherlands.

Chapter 10
Koseret (Lippia Javania)

- Van Wyk, B., Van Oudtshoorn, B., Gericke, N. 1997. Medicinal Plants of Southern Africa. Briza, Pretoria.

- Van Wyk, B., Gericke, N. 2000. People's plants: A guide to useful plants of Southern Africa. Briza, Pretoria.

- Pooley, E. 1998. A filed guide to Wild Flowers. Kwazulu-Natal and Eastern Region. Natal Flora Publications Trust, Durban.

- Van Wyk, B., Malan, S. 1997. Field guide to the Wild Flowers of the Highveld. Struik, Cape Town.

- Fox, F.W., Norwood Young, M.E. 1983. Food from the Veld: Edible wild plants of Southern Africa. Delta Books, Cape Town.

- Mitchell Watt, J., Breyer-Brandwijk, M.G. 1962. The Medicinal and Poisonous Plants of Southern and Eastern Africa. E. & S. Livingstone Ltd., Edinburgh and London.

- Roberts, M. 1990. Indigenous Healing Plants. Southern Book Publishers.

Chapter 11
Kundo Berbere (Black Pepper)

- http://www.whfoods.com/genpage.php?tname=foodspice&dbid=74

- Abila B, Richens A, Davies JA. Anticonvulsant effects of extracts of the west African black pepper, Piper guineense. J Ethnopharmacol 1993 Jun;39(2):113-7. 1993. PMID:16400.

- Ao P, Hu S, Zhao A. [Essential oil analysis and trace element study of the roots of Piper nigrum L.]. Zhongguo Zhong Yao Za Zhi 1998 Jan;23(1):42-3, 63. 1998. PMID:16370.

- Calucci L, Pinzino C, Zandomeneghi M et al. Effects of gamma-irradiation on the free radical and antioxidant contents in nine aromatic herbs and spices. J Agric Food Chem 2003 Feb 12; 51(4):927-34. 2003.

- Dorman HJ, Deans SG. Antimicrobial agents from plants: antibacterial activity of plant volatile oils. J Appl Microbiol 2000 Feb;88(2):308-16. 2000. PMID:16390.

- Ensminger AH, Ensminger, ME, Kondale JE, Robson JRK. Foods & Nutriton Encyclopedia. Pegus Press, Clovis, California. 1983.

- Ensminger AH, Esminger M. K. J. e. al. Food for Health: A Nutrition Encyclopedia. Clovis, California: Pegus Press; 1986. 1986. PMID:15210.

Chapter 12
Mitmita (Bird's Eye Chili)

- https://ethnomed.org/clinical/nutrition/
  the-traditional-foods-of-the-central-ethiopian
- Agren, G., A1mgard,G., Mellander, 0., Vahiquist, B., Bjornesjo, K.B.,
  Hofvander, Y., Jacobsson, K., Knutsson, K.E., Mellbin, T., and Selinus,
  R.: Children's Nutrition Unit - an Ethio-Swedish project in the field of
  health. Ethiopian Medical Journal, 1966:5, 5-13.
- Agren, C., Gibson, R.: Food Composition Table for use in Ethiopia.
  SIDA, Stockholm 1968.
- 3.Hofvander, Y.: Haematological investigations in Ethiopia with special
  reference to a high iron intake. Acta Med. Scand. Suppl. 494, 1968
- Analysis carried out in the Jones and Amos Laboratory in London.
- Levine, D.: Wax and gold. London 1965
- Knutsson, K.E., Selinus, R.: Fasting in Ethiopia-an Anthropological and
  Nutritional Study. American J. Clin. Nutr. June 1970.

Chapter 13
Netch Azmud (Bishop's Weed)

- http://www.drugs.com/npp/bishop-s-weed.html
- Boskabady MH, Shaikhi J. Inhibitory effect of Carum copticum on hista-
  mine (H 1) receptors of isolated guinea-pig tracheal chains. J Ethnophar-
  macol . 2000;69:217-227
- Chopra RN. Chopra's Indigenous Drug of India . 2nd ed. Calcutta:
  Academic Publishers; 1982:93-94.
- Biswas NR, Gupta SK, Das GK, et al. Evaluation of Ophthacare eye
  drops—a herbal formulation in the management of various ophthalmic
  disorders. Phytother Res . 2001;15:618-620.
- Thangham C, Dhananjayan R. Antiinflammatory potential of the seeds of
  Carum copticum Linn. Indian J of Pharmacol . 2003;35:388-391.
- Khan MA. Protective effects of Arque-Ajeeb on acute experimental diar-
  rhoea in rats. BMC Compl Altern Med . 2004;4:8.
- Ishikawah T, Sega Y, Kitajima J. Water-soluable constituents of ajowan.
  Chem Pharm Bull . 2001;49:840-844.
- Garg S, et al. A new glucoside from Trachyspermum ammi . Fitoterapia .
  1998;6:511-512.
- Ethiopia and their indigenous uses. J Essent Oil Res . 1993:5:465-479.

- Nagalakshmi S, et al. Studies on chemical and technological aspects of ajowan (Trachyspermum ammi syn. Carum copticum). J Food Sci Technol . 2000;37:277-281.
- Choudhury S, et al. Composition of the seed oil of Trachyspermum ammi (L.) Sprague from northeast India. J Essent Oil Res . 1998;10:588-590.
- Chialva F, et al. Essential oil constituents of Trachyspermum copticum (L.) Link fruits. J Essent Oil Res . 1993;5:105-106.
- De M, Krishna De A, Banerjee AB. Antimicrobial screening of some Indian spices. Phytother Res . 1999;13:616-618.

Chapter 14
Netch Shinkoort (Garlic)

- http://lpi.oregonstate.edu/mic/food-beverages/garlic
- Lawson LD. Garlic: a review of its medicinal effects and indicated active compounds. In: Lawson LD, Bauer R, eds. Phytomedicines of Europe: Chemistry and Biological Activity. Washington, D. C.: American Chemical Society; 1998:177-209.
- Block E. The chemistry of garlic and onions. Sci Am. 1985;252(3):114-119. (PubMed)
- Blumenthal M. Herb Sales Down 7.4 Percent in Mainstream Market. HerbalGram: American Botanical Council; 2005:63.
- Tapiero H, Townsend DM, Tew KD. Organosulfur compounds from alliaceae in the prevention of human pathologies. Biomed Pharmacother. 2004;58(3):183-193. (PubMed)
- Lawson LD, Wang ZJ. Allicin and allicin-derived garlic compounds increase breath acetone through allyl methyl sulfide: use in measuring allicin bioavailability. J Agric Food Chem. 2005;53(6):1974-1983. (PubMed)
- Germain E, Auger J, Ginies C, Siess MH, Teyssier C. *In vivo* metabolism of diallyl disulphide in the rat: identification of two new metabolites. Xenobiotica. 2002;32(12):1127-1138. (PubMed)
- Lachmann G, Lorenz D, Radeck W, Steiper M. [The pharmacokinetics of the S35 labeled labeled garlic constituents alliin, allicin and vinyldithiine]. Arzneimittelforschung. 1994;44(6):734-743. (PubMed)
- de Rooij BM, Boogaard PJ, Rijksen DA, Commandeur JN, Vermeulen NP. Urinary excretion of N-acetyl-S-allyl-L-cysteine upon garlic consumption by human volunteers. Arch Toxicol. 1996;70(10):635-639. (PubMed)

- Jandke J, Spiteller G. Unusual conjugates in biological profiles originating from consumption of onions and garlic. J Chromatogr. 1987;421(1):1-8. (PubMed)

- Kodera Y, Suzuki A, Imada O, et al. Physical, chemical, and biological properties of s-allylcysteine, an amino acid derived from garlic. J Agric Food Chem. 2002;50(3):622-632. (PubMed)

- Steiner M, Li W. Aged garlic extract, a modulator of cardiovascular risk factors: a dose-finding study on the effects of AGE on platelet functions. J Nutr. 2001;131(3s):980S-984S. (PubMed)

- Gebhardt R, Beck H. Differential inhibitory effects of garlic-derived organosulfur compounds on cholesterol biosynthesis in primary rat hepatocyte cultures. Lipids. 1996;31(12):1269-1276. (PubMed)

Chapter 15
Senafich (Mustard Seed)

- http://www.whfoods.com/genpage.php?tname=foodspice&dbid=106

- Ensminger AH, Ensminger, ME, Kondale JE, Robson JRK. Foods & Nutriton Encyclopedia. Pegus Press, Clovis, California. 1983.

- Ensminger AH, Esminger M. K. J. e. al. Food for Health: A Nutrition Encyclopedia. Clovis, California: Pegus Press; 1986. 1986. PMID:15210.

- Fortin, Francois, Editorial Director. The Visual Foods Encyclopedia. Macmillan, New York. 1996.

- Grieve M. A Modern Herbal. Dover Publications, New York. 1971.

- Thimmulappa RK, Mai KH, Srisuma S et al. Identification of Nrf2-regulated genes induced by the chemopreventive agent sulforaphane by oligonucleotide microarray. Cancer Res 2002 Sep 15;62(18):5196-5203. 2002.

- Wood, Rebecca. The Whole Foods Encyclopedia. New York, NY: Prentice-Hall Press; 1988. 1988. PMID:15220.

Chapter 16
Shinkoort (red, yellow, and white)

- http://www.whfoods.com/references/index.php?tname=foodspice&dbid=45

- Ali M, Thomson M, Afzal M. Garlic and onions: their effect on eicosanoid metabolism and its clinical relevance. Prostaglandins Leukot Essent Fatty Acids. 2000 Feb;62(2):55-73. Review. 2000.

- Azuma K, Minami Y, Ippoushi K et al. Lowering effects of onion intake on oxidative stress biomarkers in streptozotocin-induced diabetic rats. J Clin Biochem Nutr. 2007 Mar;40(2):131-40. 2007.

• Borjihan B, Ogita A, Fujita KI et al. The Cyclic Organosulfur Compound Zwiebelane A from Onion (Allium cepa) Functions as an Enhancer of Polymyxin B in Fungal Vacuole Disruption. Planta Med. 2010 May 19. [Epub ahead of print]. 2010.

• Brat P, George S, Bellamy A, et al. Daily Polyphenol Intake in France from Fruit and Vegetables. J. Nutr. 136:2368-2373, September 2006. 2006.

• Chun OK, Chung SJ, and Song WO. Estimated dietary flavonoid intake and major food sources of U.S. adults. J Nutr. 2007 May;137(5):1244-52. 2007.

• Dorant E, van den Brandt PA, Goldbohm RA. A prospective cohort study on the relationship between onion and leek consumption, garlic supplement use and the risk of colorectal carcinoma in The Netherlands. Carcinogenesis 1996 Mar;17(3):477-84. 1996. PMID:13660.

• Eady CC, Kamoi T, Kato M et al. Silencing onion lachrymatory factor synthase causes a significant change in the sulfur secondary metabolite profile. Plant Physiol. 2008 Aug;147(4):2096-106. 2008.

• El-Aasr M, Fujiwara Y, Takeya M et al. Onionin A from Allium cepa inhibits macrophage activation. J Nat Prod. 2010 Jul 23;73(7):1306-8. 2010.

• Fukushima S, Takada N, Hori T, Wanibuchi H. Cancer prevention by organosulfur compounds from garlic and onion. J Cell Biochem Suppl 1997;27:100-5. 1997. PMID:13650.

• Galeone C, Pelucchi C, Levi F, Negri E, Franceschi S, Talamini R, Giacosa A, La Vecchia C. Onion and garlic use and human cancer. *Am J Clin Nutr*. 2006 Nov;84(5):1027-32. 2006. PMID:17093154.

• Galeone C, Pelucchi C, Talamini R et al. Onion and garlic intake and the odds of benign prostatic hyperplasia. Urology. 2007 Oct;70(4):672-6. 2007.

• Galeone C, Tavani A, Pelucchi C, et al. Allium vegetable intake and risk of acute myocardial infarction in Italy. Eur J Nutr. 2009 Mar;48(2):120-3. 2009.

• Gates MA, Tworoger SS, Hecht JL, De Vivo I, Rosner B, Hankinson SE. A prospective study of dietary flavonoid intake and incidence of epithelial ovarian cancer. Int J Cancer. 2007 Apr 30; [Epub ahead of print]. 2007. PMID:17471564.

• Gautam S, Platel K and Srinivasan K. Higher bioaccessibility of iron and zinc from food grains in the presence of garlic and onion. J Agric Food Chem. 2010 Jul 28;58(14):8426-9. 2010.

- Imai S, Tsuge N, Tomotake M et al. Plant biochemistry: an onion enzyme that makes the eyes water. Nature. London: Oct 17, 2002. Vol. 419, Iss. 6908; p. 685. 2002.
- Kim JH. Anti-bacterial action of onion (Allium cepa L.) extracts against oral pathogenic bacteria. J Nihon Univ Sch Dent. 1997 Sep;39(3):136-41. 1997.
- Kook S, Kim GH and Choi K. The antidiabetic effect of onion and garlic in experimental diabetic rats: meta-analysis. J Med Food. 2009 Jun;12(3):552-60. 2009.
- Matheson EM, Mainous AG 3rd and Carnemolla MA. The association between onion consumption and bone density in perimenopausal and post-menopausal non-Hispanic white women 50 years and older. Menopause. 2009 Jul-Aug;16(4):756-9. 2009.

Chapter 17
Tena Adam (Rue)

- http://www.drugs.com/npp/rue.html
- Furniss D, Adams T. Herb of grace: an unusual cause of phytophotoderma-titis mimicking burn injury. J Burn Care Res . 2007;28(5):767-769.
- lChevallier A . The Encyclopedia of Medicinal Plants . New York, NY: DK Publishing; 1996:262-263.
- Conway GA , Slocumb JC . Plants used as abortifacients and emmena-gogues by Spanish New Mexicans . J Ethnopharmacol . 1979;1(3):241-261.
- Pollio A, De Natale A, Appetiti E, Aliotta G, Touwaide A. Continuity and change in the Mediterranean medical tradition: Ruta spp. (rutacecae) in Hippocratic medicine and present practices. J Ethnopharmacol .
- Duke J . CRC Handbook of Medicinal Herbs . Boca Raton, FL: CRC Press; 1989:417-418.
- Minker E , Bartha C , Koltai M , Rózsa Z , Szendrei K , Reisch J . Effect of secondary substances isolated from the Ruta graveolens L. on the coronary smooth muscle . Acta Pharm Hung . 1980;50(1):7-11.
- Tyler VE . The New Honest Herbal: A Sensible Guide to the Use of Herbs and Related Remedies . Philadelphia, PA: GF Stickley Co; 1987.
- Wolters B , Eilert U . Antimicrobial substances in callus cultures of Ruta graveolens . Planta Med . 1981;43(2):166-174.

- Verzár-Petri G , Csedö K , Möllmann K , Szendrei K , Reisch J . Fluorescence microscopic investigations on the localisation of acridone alkaloids in the organs of Ruta graveolens [in German]. Planta Med . 1976;29(4):370-375.
- Spoerke DG . Herbal Medications . Santa Barbara, CA: Woodbridge Press; 1980.
- Haesen JP , Vörde Sive Vörding JG , Kho KF . Isolation and identification of xanthotoxin from the underground parts of Ruta graveolens . Planta Med . 1971;19(3):285-289.
- Zobel AM , Brown SA . Determination of furanocoumarins on the leaf surface of Ruta graveolens with an improved extraction technique. J Nat Prod . 1988;51(5):941-946.
- Paulini H , Popp R , Schimmer O , Ratka O , Röder E . Isogravacridonchlorine: a potent and direct acting frameshift mutagen from the roots of Ruta graveolens . Planta Med . 1991;57(1):59-61.
- Montagu M , Petit-Paly G , Levillain P , et al. Synchronous fluorescence spectrometry and identification of dihydrofuro[2,3-b]quinolinium alkaloids biosynthesized by Ruta graveolens cultures in vitro. Pharmazie . 1989;44:342-34

Chapter 18
Tikur Azmude (Black Cumin)

- http://healthimpactnews.com/2014/ black-cumin-seeds-better-than-drugs-a-look-at-the-science/
- Ahmad A1, Husain A, Mujeeb M, Khan SA, Najmi AK, Siddique NA, Damanhouri ZA, Anwar F, Kishore K.; "A review on therapeutic potential of Nigella sativa: A miracle herb," Asian Pac J Trop Biomed., 2013 May, PMID: 23646296.
- Salem ML.; "Immunomodulatory and therapeutic properties of the Nigella sativa L. seed," Int Immunopharmacol. 2005 Dec, PMID: 16275613.
- Entok E1, Ustuner MC, Ozbayer C, Tekin N, Akyuz F, Yangi B, Kurt H, Degirmenci I, Gunes HV.; "Anti-inflammatuar and anti-oxidative effects of Nigella sativa L.: 18FDG-PET imaging of inflammation," Mol Biol Rep. 2014 May, PMID: 24474661.
- Vanamala J1, Kester AC, Heuberger AL, Reddivari L.; "Mitigation of obesity-promoted diseases by Nigella sativa and thymoquinone," Plant Foods Hum Nutr. 2012 Jun, PMID: 22477645.

- [Hasani-Ranjbar S1, Jouyandeh Z, Abdollahi M.; "A systematic review of anti-obesity medicinal plants – an update," J Diabetes Metab Disord., 2013 June 19, PMID: 23777875.
- Farzaneh E1, Nia FR2, Mehrtash M2, Mirmoeini FS3, Jalilvand M1.; "The Effects of 8-week Nigella sativa Supplementation and Aerobic Training on Lipid Profile and VO2 max in Sedentary Overweight Females," Int J Prev Med., 2014 February, PMID: 24627749.
- Oysu C1, Tosun A1, Yilmaz HB2, Sahin-Yilmaz A3, Korkmaz D1, Kara-aslan A1.; "Topical Nigella Sativa for nasal symptoms in elderly," Auris Nasus Larynx. 2014 Jun, PMID: 24398317

Chapter 19
Timiz (Long Pepper)

- http://en.wikipedia.org/wiki/Long_pepper
- Sesha Iyengar, T.R (1989). "Dravidian India". ISBN 9788120601352.
- Rawlinson, H. G (2001-05-01). "Intercourse Between India and the Western World: From the Earliest Times of the Fall of Rome".ISBN 9788120615496.
- J Barnett, Lionel D (1999-01-01). "Antiquities of India: An Account of the History and Culture of Ancient Hindustan".ISBN 9788171564422.
- Maguelonne Toussaint-Samat, Anthea Bell, tr. *The History of Food*, revised ed. 2009, p.
- Philippe and Mary Hyman, "Connaissez-vous le poivre long?" *L'Histoire* no. 24 (June 1980).
- "Novel compound selectively kills cancer cells by blocking their response to oxidative stress". Science Daily. July 15, 2011.

Appendix A
Free Radicals and Antioxidants

- Halliwell, B. and Gutteridge John M.C. Free Radicals in Biology and
- Medicine, Oxford: Clarendon Press, 1989, pp. 454-458.
- Quillin, Patrick, Ph.D., Healing Nutrients, Chicago, New York: Contemporary Books Inc., 1987, p. 335.
- Ershoff, B.H., American Journal of Clinical Nutrition, vol. 27,1974, p. 1395.
- Ershoff, B.H., American Journalof ClinicalNutrition, vol. 41, 1976, p. 949.

Selenium

- Bosco, Dominick, The People's Guide to fitamins and Minerals, Chicago:
- Contemporary Books, 1980, p. 249.

Ethiopian Traditional and Herbal Medications and their Interactions with Conventional Drugs[9]

Herb/Spice	Common Uses	Drugs Affected	Mechanism	Consequences
Basil *Ocimum basilicum* Besobila (A) Zahahene (O)	• Mostly culinary • Medicinal: headache, insect repellent, malaria	• Anticoagulants • Hypoglycemic agents	• Oil extract has been found to increase clotting time • Synergistic interaction with insulin and oral hypoglycemic agents	• Increased chance of bleeding • May further lower blood glucose
Black Mustard *Brassica nigra* Senafitch (A) (T) Senafitcha (O)	• Culinary use • Medicinal use: stomach ache, constipation, bloating, amoebic dysentery and abortifacient • Also used for wound dressing.		• Mustard seeds and oil- may increase production of stomach acid • Allyl thiocyanate is an irritant that can cause severe burns and tissue necrosis (Fullas 2003) • High concentration of Vitamin K	• Interferes with antacid treatment • Antagonizes effects of Warfarin
Black seed *Nigella sativa* Tiqur azmud (A) Awoseta (T) Gura (O)	• Culinary uses • Medicinal: headache, stomachache, abortifacient		• Platelet aggregation inhibition • Increases pancreatic insulin secretion • Evidence in animal studies of reduced arterial blood pressure by increasing vasodilation and inhibiting contraction. • Evidence of pregnancy inhibitor in rats (Fullas, 2003)	• Increased risk of bleeding • Synergistic action with medication that lowers blood pressure and blood glucose
Capsicum pepper **Cayenne pepper** *Capsicum annum* Berbere (A)	• Mostly culinary • Medicinal: stomach ache, antimicrobial		• Capsaicin may inhibit platelet aggregation • Increases production of catecholamines • Decreases blood glucose levels and stimulates insulin release	• Increased risk of bleeding • May counteract mechanism of antihypertensives • Recorded incidences of increased cough when combined with ACE inhibitors
Cinnamon *Cinnamomum zelanicum* Qarafa (A) Crefte (T) Carafu (O)	• Culinary • Medicinal: treatment for cold symptoms		• Claimed to increase stomach acid • Experimental evidence of tetracycline dissolution rate interference	• May counteract antacids • May inhibit tetracycline action

9   Author(s): Alevtina Gall, BS, BA; Zerihun Shenkute, RPh
Reviewer(s): David Kiefer, MD; J. Carey Jackson, MD, MPH, MA
Date Authored: November 03, 2009

Herb/Spice	Common Uses	Drugs Affected	Mechanism	Consequences
Coriander *Coriandrum sativum* Dimbelal (A) Zagada (T) Shucar (O)	• Mostly culinary • Medicinal: stomach ache and colic		• Unknown, but has been shown to be effective in treating stomach upset (Fullas 2003)	• *Lowers blood sugar levels;
Cumin *Cuminum cyminum* Ensilal (A) Kemano (T) Hawaja (O)	• Mostly culinary		• May have hypoglycemic properties • May have anticoagulating properties	• *Hypoglycemia • *Increased risk of bleeding
Dingetegna(A) *No common English name* Taverniera abyssinica	• Medicinal only for stomach upset • Fever reduction		• Antispasmodic properties may affect absorption of medication	• Decreased absorption of medication
Fenugreek *Trigonella foenumgraceum* Abish (A) Halbata (O)	• Mostly culinary • Medicinal: stomachache, antispasmodic, powder used for wound dressing		• Studies have shown that fenugreek acts synergistically with blood glucose lowering drugs • Decreases total cholesterol and LDLs • Alters T3 and T4 levels • Anticoagulating properties	• *Hypoglycemia • *Lower cholesterol • *Reduced intestinal absorbance of medication • *Increased risk of bleeding
Flaxseed and flaxseed oil *Linum usitatissimum* Telba (A) Lina (T) Konfur (O)	• Medicinal: purgative, diuretic, laxative		• Flaxseed and oil decrease platelet aggregation, increase effects of lipid lowering and hypoglycemic agents • Lignans (phyto-estrogens) from flaxseed (not oil) possess hormonal effects • As a bulk forming laxative, flaxseed may bind to cardiac glycosides and other orally administered medications and prevent absorption • Flaxseed enhances laxative effects of stool softeners	• *Increased risk of bleeding • Reduced intestinal absorbance of oral medication; as any fiber source • Increased risk of hypoglycemia • Possible dehydration from increased laxative effects of flaxseed (Due to absorption of liquid by fiber. It is important for patient to drink enough water.)

Herb/Spice	Common Uses	Drugs Affected	Mechanism	Consequences
Garlic *Allium sativum* Nech shinkrut (A) Tsada shgurti (T) Qullabbiiadii (O)	• Culinary • Medicinal: common cold, malaria, cough, pulmonary TB, hypertension, wounds, STDs, asthma, parasitic infections, toothache, diabetes, hemorrhoids		• May be additive with cholesterol-lowering drugs • Hypertensive activity but it is not known if this effect is antihypertensive drug additive • Decreases T3 and T4 levels • May have blood thinning properties	• *Possible increased risk of bleeding; • *Reverses effects of orally administered thyroxine
Ginger *Zingiber officinale* Zingibil (A) (T)	• Culinary • Medicinal: stomachache, cough, fever, influenza		• Irritates gastric mucosa • Decreases platelet aggregation	• *Inhibits antacid therapy • *Increased risk of bleeding
Khat *Catha edulis* Chat (A) Ciut (T) (O)	• Mostly recreational • Medicinal: stimulant, mental illness, gonorrhea, common cold		• Cathinone (active ingredient) may act synergistically with amphetamines • Tannins (component of Khat) complexes with ß-lactam antibiotics	• Possible additive effect with amphetamines • Decreases absorbability of b-lactam antibiotics • Lowers seizure threshold, • Increases b.p and heart rate and induces cardiac arrythmias.
Peppermint *Mentha piperita* Nanna (A) (O) Semhal (T)	• Medicinal: common cold, headache		• Inhibits gut wall metabolism of felodipine and simvastatin • Decreases absorption of non-heme iron • Reduces Warfarin internal normalized ratio to subtherapeutic levels	• Increased risk of clots if patient is in a hypercoagulable state • Non-absorption of felodipine, simvostatin and iron • Increases GERD symptoms unless taken as enteric-coated capsules
Rue *Ruta chalepensis* Tenadam (A) (T) Talatam (O)	• Medicinal: common cold, stomachache, diarrhea, influenza		• No major interactions reported • 5-methoxy psoralen content of rue may increase phototoxic response • May interact with Warfarin	• Anticoagulant effects maybe additive
Turmeric *Curcuma longa* Ird (A) (O)	• Mostly culinary • Medicinal: used topically for "crying eyes" in children		• Has been shown to inhibit platelet aggregation *in vitro* • Curcuminoids and sesquiterpene components of turmeric have hypoglycemic	• Increased risk of bleeding (theoretical risk; has not been demonstrated) • Reduces blood sugar levels

Ethiopian Spice and Teff flour suppliers

Brundo Ethiopian Spices
6419 Telegraph Ave.
Oakland, CA 94609
(510) 298-7101
www.brundo.com
info@brundo.com

Selam Import
2294 S. Bascom Ave.
Campbell, CA 95008
Phone: 408.377.3090
Fax: 408.377.1099
selamimport@yahoo.com

Ethio Imports, LLC
EthiopianSpices.com
2804 Taylorsville Rd.
Louisville, KY 40205
502-459-6301
502-243-5472
Order@ethiopianspices.com

Workinesh Spice Blends
3451 W. Burnsville Parkway
Minneapolis, MN 55337

Abyssinian Market
500 Woodcroft Parkway
Durham, NC 27713
www.abyssiniamarket.com
CustomerService@AbyssiniaMarket.com

For a more extensive list, go to:
http://www.pitt.edu/~kloman/markets.html

website: https://ethiopianfood.wordpress.com/
Harry Kloman has a great website that offers extensive information on just about
anything Ethiopian. Check it out!

Cook books

Exotic Ethiopian Cooking
by Daniel Mesfin

Cooking with Imaye:
Ethiopian Cooking Straight from Mom's Kitchen
By Lena Deresse

Ethiopian Cooking in the American Kitchen
by Tizita Ayele

Credits

Back cover:
Beer and glass:
http://intoxicology.net/drinking-in-ethiopia/

Tea in a glass
https://www.pinterest.com/chrislbarton/ethiopian-drink/

coffee in a cup
https://fulbrightmekelle.wordpress.com/2014/04/06/starbacks-coffee/

Nitre Kibehh
http://africanchop.com/smallchop/basic-foods-ethiopian-cooking/

The tray of spices at the bottom came from:
http://www.maximumhealth.pw/product-category/herbs/

The three juice drinks:
http://boomdeyada.ca/2011/06/food-drink-fun-in-ethiopia/

Ethiopian honey wine—3 glasses and red bottled wine, Maria Tenaye
https://www.pinterest.com/tenaye777/good-food-and-drinks-from-ethiopia/

The array of spices that appear on the back of The four Pillars
http://www.chercherrestaurant.com/take-out/chercher-market/

Mitten berbere on the cover
http://www.mymcmedia.org/local-ethiopian-business-works-to-empower-women/

Tella in clay tumbler
http://pixhder.com/traditional+ethiopian+drinks

Coffee ceremony
http://www.couponraja.in/theroyale/ethiopia-intriguing-cuisine-ambrosial-beverages/

Front cover:
Mesob front cover picture:
http://natural-history.uoregon.edu/ethiopian08

The first tray of foods came from:
http://migrationology.com/2014/02/ethiopian-food-guide/

The middle tray of foods came from:
http://cool-food-photo.com/ethiopian-food.html

PART VII
Index

Want to learn about the Ethiopian people and their culture? Read the *Desta* series!

www.amazon.com or www.gettyambau.com

Desta: To Whom the Lions Bow—Volume 3

A winner of Moonbeam's 2014 Children's Book Award

Desta and the Winds of Washaa Umera—Volume 2

Featured in the February 2014 issue of Kirkus Magazine

Desta and King Solomon's Coin of Magic and Fortune—Volume 1

A winner of moonbeam's 2010 Children's Book Award and Independent Publishers' 2011 Children's Book Award

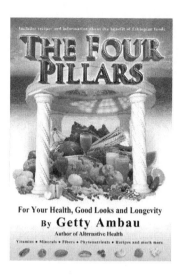

For Your Health, Good Looks and Longevity
By Getty Ambau
Author of Alternative Health
Vitamins • Minerals • Fibers • Phytonutrients • Recipes and much more

Reviews

"This is an outstanding book! It's written with such simplicity and clarity that anybody should be able to understand the information and use it to make appropriate dietary choices. . . ." **Herbert Jacobs, M.D.**

"For anyone interested in optimizing health, improving exercise performance, and preventing diseases, this book is a must read."
John Riley, M.D.

"This great book presents a wealth of information to all those who wish to achieve and maintain optimum health. The incorporation of phytonutrients, herbs and spices as part of one's daily nutrition is a novel idea that is both intriguing and appealing. They may have much to offer to our wellness and longevity."
Michael Jason, M.D.

"This is a remarkable book in many ways. I highly recommend it for anyone who has an interest in proper nutrition."
Diane Radcliff, reader

"This . . . is not the kind of book you can pick up, read and then forget. It's something you want to live with for the rest of your life. It's that good a book, but then again, only if you truly want to have a healthy life."
Denniger Bolton, Author

About the Author

Author Getty Ambau was born in Ethiopia. He first came to the United States as a foreign exchange student, where he studied one year at a high school in Ohio. Later he entered Yale University, where he majored in molecular biophysics and biochemistry and Economics. After he graduated, he worked as a research chemist, earned a graduate degree in business and ran his own companies, but above all, writing has always been his inner calling. He is the author of two health and nutrition books, which became international bestsellers.

Getty is also the creator of the Desta series (novels), which have received recognition and won three awards. He lives in San Francisco Bay Area with his wife and an adorable terrier named, Scruffy.

59959281R00125

Made in the USA
Middletown, DE
23 December 2017